Vocabulary WORKS

Level E

Joy Tweedt   Craig Tweedt   &   Dr. Alvin Granowsky

ISBN 0-8136-1723-5
Printed in the United States of America
14 15 16   08 07 06

Modern Curriculum Press

Pearson Learning Group

1-800-321-3106
www.pearsonlearning.com

TABLE OF CONTENTS

VOLLEYBALL SERVES UP FUN

Volleyball is a fast game. It starts when a player puts the ball into play from a corner of the court. The ball is **served** underhand or **overhand**. Then it is up to the team on the other side of the net to keep the ball in the air. They try to send it back across the net so that it lands on their opponent's court.

Volleyball was first played in 1895 at the YMCA in Holyoke, Massachusetts. People were coming there for indoor **physical education**, and the director wanted a new game in which more people could **participate**. He found it in volleyball.

A **gymnasium** is a good place to play volleyball, but a backyard or beach will do. Although volleyball courts attract players of all sizes and ages, **height** is an **asset** for power players. Karch Kiraly, a member of the US Olympic Volleyball Team, uses his height to achieve a forty-inch **vertical** jump. It's no wonder he helped bring home the gold in the 1984 and 1988 Olympics!

MAIN IDEA SETS UP STORY

What is the story mainly about?

Check the best answer.

❑ Karch Kiraly

❑ games played across a net

❑ beach games

❑ the game of volleyball

ALPHABET AT YOUR SERVICE

Write the New Words in alphabetical order.

New Words

- served
- overhand
- volleyball
- physical
- education
- participate
- gymnasium
- height
- asset
- vertical

1. _____   6. _____

2. _____   7. _____

3. _____   8. _____

4. _____   9. _____

5. _____   10. _____

WORDS AND MEANINGS MAKE EXCITING MATCH

Use context clues to match each New Word with its meaning. Write the correct letter on each line.

___ 1. served

___ 2. overhand

___ 3. volleyball

___ 4. physical

___ 5. education

___ 6. participate

___ 7. gymnasium

___ 8. height

___ 9. asset

___ 10. vertical

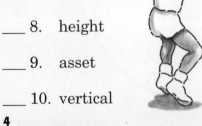

a. put a ball into play during a game

b. perpendicular to the horizon

c. with the hand or hands above the head

d. a relatively great distance from bottom to top

e. a game in which two teams hit a ball across a high net; a type of ball

f. take part in

g. having to do with the body

h. the process of developing knowledge or skill

i. a place for physical exercise

j. a trait or quality that gives advantage or profit

NEW WORDS FINISH SENTENCES

Use the New Words to finish these sentences.

1. Lines of latitude are horizontal, but lines of longitude are _____ .

2. A good _____ will prepare you for a successful career.

3. My mother goes to a _____ to work out twice a week.

4. My friends and I get together at the beach to play _____ .

5. The _____ of the new building downtown is amazing.

6. The marathon race is a test of _____ endurance.

7. I prefer baseball to softball because I like to pitch _____ .

8. It is fun to _____ in many different sports.

9. Her first try went out of bounds, so she _____ again.

10. His friendly personality was a great _____ in his job.

SUFFIXES AT WORK

A **suffix** is a word part that can be added to the end of a root word. Adding a suffix changes the meaning of a root word.

The suffix **al** can mean <u>of</u>, <u>like</u>, or <u>act of</u>.

Add the suffix <u>al</u> to the root words below. Then write the meaning of the new word. You may need to change the spelling of some words. The first one is done for you.

Root Word	Root + Suffix	Word Meaning
a. deny	<u>denial</u>	<u>act of denying</u>
b. arrive	_____	_____
c. music	_____	_____
d. magic	_____	_____
e. refuse	_____	_____
f. dismiss	_____	_____

ANALOGIES MAKE MEANINGFUL RELATIONSHIPS

 Analogies show the relationship between things.

fur is to **bear** as **scales** is to **fish**

plant is to **soil** as **fish** is to **water**

Use the New Words to finish these analogies.

1. _____ is to <u>throw</u> as <u>backhand</u> is to <u>hit</u>

2. <u>mind</u> is to <u>mental</u> as <u>body</u> is to _____

3. _____ is to <u>high</u> as <u>weight</u> is to <u>heavy</u>

4. <u>unfavorable</u> is to <u>loss</u> as <u>valuable</u> is to _____

5. _____ is to <u>height</u> as <u>horizontal</u> is to <u>width</u>

6. _____ is to <u>game</u> as <u>join</u> is to <u>team</u>

> **New Words**
>
> physical
>
> participate
>
> asset
>
> height
>
> vertical
>
> overhand

PERSONAL BEST

 Pretend that you are a famous athlete. Write a story telling about your most dramatic experience during a game.

These questions will help guide your writing:

- What led up to your dramatic experience?
- How would you describe your performance?
- How did the experience affect the game?

Use at least four New Words in your story.

VOLLEYBALL TIDBITS

> Top fashion model Gabrielle Reece is also a professional volleyball player.

> Wilt Chamberlain and Tom Selleck are avid volleyball players.

DIVE INTO READING

READ:

- *Go For It: Volleyball* by Bill Gutman. (Grey Castle Press, 1990)
- *Be the Best: Volleyball* by Charles Bracken. (Troll Associates, 1990)

Spike over the test!

TEST-TAKING SECRETS REVEALED

When looking for a word that means the opposite of a given word, don't be fooled by a choice that means the same.

Read each group of words. Select the word or words that mean the opposite of the underlined word. Fill in the circle for the answer at the bottom of the page.

1   a <u>vertical</u> line

    A horizontal   **C** base
    B upright   **D** long

2   a player's <u>asset</u>

    A skill   **C** talent
    B possession **D** disadvantage

3   choose to <u>participate</u>

    A help with   **C** play
    B join in   **D** withdraw

4   an <u>overhand</u> hit

    A hard   **C** underhand
    B dishonest   **D** punch

Complete each definition with the best word. Fill in the circle for the answer at the bottom of the page.

5   Exercise of the body rather than the mind is called . . . .

    A volleyball
    B physical
    C gymnasium
    D education

6   The tallness of a person is called . . . .

    A asset
    B height
    C weight
    D upright

7   A large room where some sports are played is a . . . .

    A vertical
    B gymnasium
    C volleyball
    D asset

8   Training in various skills and knowledge is called . . . .

    A vertical
    B physical
    C volleyball
    D education

9   A line that is drawn straight up and down is called . . . .

    A overhand
    B physical
    C horizontal
    D vertical

10   A game in which a ball is hit across a net is called . . . .

    A overhand
    B vertical
    C volleyball
    D gymnasium

11   To have started the ball in play in volleyball is to have . . . .

    A overhand
    B served
    C volleyed
    D involved

12   To hit the ball with hands over the head is to hit it . . . .

    A height
    B overhand
    C overhead
    D vertical

ANSWERS

1 Ⓐ Ⓑ Ⓒ Ⓓ	4 Ⓐ Ⓑ Ⓒ Ⓓ	7 Ⓐ Ⓑ Ⓒ Ⓓ	10 Ⓐ Ⓑ Ⓒ Ⓓ
2 Ⓐ Ⓑ Ⓒ Ⓓ	5 Ⓐ Ⓑ Ⓒ Ⓓ	8 Ⓐ Ⓑ Ⓒ Ⓓ	11 Ⓐ Ⓑ Ⓒ Ⓓ
3 Ⓐ Ⓑ Ⓒ Ⓓ	6 Ⓐ Ⓑ Ⓒ Ⓓ	9 Ⓐ Ⓑ Ⓒ Ⓓ	12 Ⓐ Ⓑ Ⓒ Ⓓ

CAN YOU SPEAK SPANISH?

Imagine this. Your friend invites you over for the weekend. As the two of you play on the **patio**, your friend's father brings out some delicious **tacos**. There are also **tortillas**, meat, vegetables, and cheese to roll into burritos for dinner.

During dinner the family talks about tomorrow's activities. "The **rodeo** is in town," your friend tells everyone. "The world champion **bronco** buster is going to put on a real show. We'd better get there **pronto** to get good seats!"

The **conversation** above is in English, right? Of course, all the words in the conversation are spoken as English words. But did you know that the words in dark type are actually Spanish words that have made their way into the English language?

There are a lot of Spanish words that are now a part of our language. Words such as **plaza, burro,** and **vanilla** are really Spanish words that have become a part of our daily speech.

Keep your ears open as you talk to Spanish-speaking friends about their language. You may find that you can speak more Spanish than you thought you could.

Sí (Yes) or No?

Are the following statements true or false?
Circle the best answer.

1. Some English words are borrowed from Spanish.

    Sí   No

2. The word *rodeo* is borrowed from Spanish.

    Sí   No

3. The word *patio* is from the French language.

    Sí   No

4. The word *rodeo* is from the German language.

    Sí   No

ALPHABET WORKS IN MANY LANGUAGES

New Words

patio

pronto

tacos

tortillas

rodeo

bronco

conversation

plaza

burro

vanilla

Write the New Words in alphabetical order.

1. _____

2. _____

3. _____

4. _____

5. _____

6. _____

7. _____

8. _____

9. _____

10. _____

WORDS AND MEANINGS MATCH

Use context clues or the glossary to match each New Word with its meaning.

Write the correct letter on each line.

____ 1. patio   a. a paved area next to a house for outdoor dining or lounging

____ 2. pronto   b. a wild or partly tamed horse

____ 3. tacos   c. right away; without delay

____ 4. tortillas   d. a flavoring used in cooking

____ 5. rodeo   e. folded tortillas with some sort of filling, usually beef or beans

____ 6. bronco   f. a public square or courtyard

____ 7. conversation   g. flat cakes or breads made of cornmeal

____ 8. plaza   h. talk between two or more people

____ 9. burro   i. a cowboy show

____ 10. vanilla   j. a small donkey

NEW WORDS FILL SENTENCE HOLES

Use the New Words to finish these sentences.

1. The bull-riding competition is the most exciting part of the _____ .

2. My brother hurt his shoulder when he went _____ riding.

3. I saw a film of Mexican cooks mixing cornmeal and water to make _____ .

4. When I make _____ , I like to add a lot of beef and beans.

5. I had an interesting _____ with my new neighbor.

6. We sat on a bench in the _____ in the middle of town.

7. In the summer my family cooks out on the _____ .

8. When dinner is ready, everyone comes to the table _____ .

9. A _____ carried our camping equipment during our visit to Mexico.

10. We also had a chance to see how _____ is made from the beans of an orchid.

DON'T BE FOOLED BY HOMONYMS

☞ **Homonyms** are words that sound alike but have different meanings and spellings.

too and **two**   **blew** and **blue**

Draw lines to connect these homonyms.

1. hire	a. knight	6. allowed	a. suite
2. capital	b. seen	7. jeans	b. peak
3. night	c. heal	8. sweet	c. aloud
4. heel	d. higher	9. peek	d. rows
5. scene	e. capitol	10. rose	e. genes

Now use the correct homonyms to finish these sentences.

a. We cheered as the climbers reached the mountain _____ .

b. Marsha will rehearse the second _____ of the play on the stage.

c. It takes several weeks for a broken bone to _____ .

d. Only employees are _____ in this section of the building.

e. Do not wash your _____ in hot water, or they will shrink.

f. The sugary icing tasted too _____ .

SOLUTION TO PUZZLE FOUND

Use the New Words to finish the crossword puzzle.

New Words
- patio
- pronto
- tacos
- tortillas
- rodeo
- bronco
- conversation
- plaza
- burro
- vanilla

ACROSS
2. a public square
3. a small donkey
4. talk between people
7. right away
8. flat cakes made of cornmeal

DOWN
1. a cowboy show
2. a paved area next to a house
3. a wild horse
5. a flavoring used in cooking
6. folded tortillas with a filling, usually beef or beans

RIDIN', ROPIN', AND RODEO

 Have you ever seen or read about a rodeo? Work with a group of your classmates to present a report on the rodeo.

These questions will help guide your writing:

- Where do rodeos take place?
- What is the history of the rodeo?
- What skills does a rodeo performer need to have?

Use at least four New Words in your report.

English to Spanish

The Spanish language also uses some English words. Did you know that the words *television, radio,* and *cassette* mean the same in Spanish as they do in English?

Speak More Spanish!

- *Activity Book in Spanish and English for Children* by Leslie Moreno. (Executive Commission, 1983)
- *The Adventures of Connie and Diego* by Maria Garcia. (Children's Press, 1987)
- *Teach Me Spanish* by Judy Mohoney and Mary Cronon. (Teach Me Publishers, 1989. Includes cassette.)
- *Spanish Is Fun, Book A* by Wald Heywood. (AMSCD, 1988)

You're ready to take the test-pronto!

SCORE HIGHER ON TESTS

Look over the entire test before you begin to see what you will be doing.

Read each sentence. Select the answer that best completes each one. Fill in the circle for the answer at the bottom of the page.

1   Add a teaspoon of ____ to the cake batter.

   A tacos
   B vanilla
   C tortillas
   D burritos

2   We keep the outdoor furniture on the ____.

   A rodeo
   B bronco
   C patio
   D plaza

3   My little sister took a ride on the ____.

   A bronco
   B burro
   C plaza
   D tortillas

4   I enjoyed a long ____ with him last summer.

   A patio
   B pronto
   C vanilla
   D conversation

5   Are you strong enough to take a ____ ride?

   A bronco
   B burro
   C rodeo
   D pronto

6   The ____ were filled with chopped meat and lettuce.

   A plazas
   B rodeos
   C tacos
   D bronco

7   The people of the town enjoyed walking through the ____ on the warm Sunday afternoon.

   A patio
   B plaza
   C burro
   D pronto

8   The ____ were made of cornmeal.

   A burros
   B tortillas
   C rodeos
   D plazas

Read each question. Select the word that best answers it. Fill in the circle for the answer at the bottom of the page.

9   Which word probably comes from the Spanish word *rodear*, which means "to surround"?

   A patio   **C** plaza
   B rodeo   **D** burro

10   Which word probably comes from the Latin word *burricus*, which means "small horse"?

   A bronco   **C** plaza
   B tacos   **D** burro

11   Which word probably comes from the Latin word *platea*, meaning "broad street"?

   A patio   **C** vanilla
   B plaza   **D** tacos

12   Which word probably comes from the Latin word *promptus*, meaning "prompt"?

   A plaza   **C** pronto
   B patio   **D** burritos

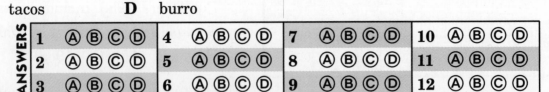

ANSWERS

1	Ⓐ Ⓑ Ⓒ Ⓓ	4	Ⓐ Ⓑ Ⓒ Ⓓ	7	Ⓐ Ⓑ Ⓒ Ⓓ	10	Ⓐ Ⓑ Ⓒ Ⓓ
2	Ⓐ Ⓑ Ⓒ Ⓓ	5	Ⓐ Ⓑ Ⓒ Ⓓ	8	Ⓐ Ⓑ Ⓒ Ⓓ	11	Ⓐ Ⓑ Ⓒ Ⓓ
3	Ⓐ Ⓑ Ⓒ Ⓓ	6	Ⓐ Ⓑ Ⓒ Ⓓ	9	Ⓐ Ⓑ Ⓒ Ⓓ	12	Ⓐ Ⓑ Ⓒ Ⓓ

SPACE TECHNOLOGY IMPROVES LIFE ON EARTH

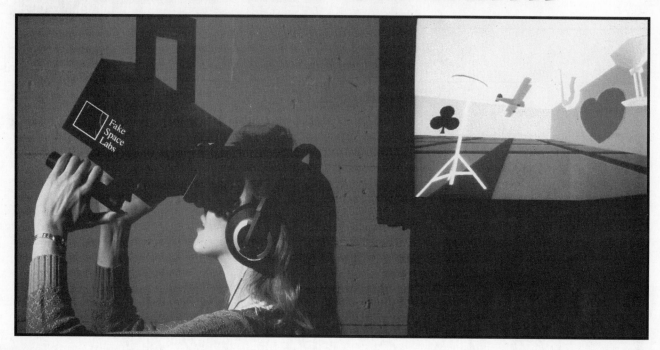

Perhaps the best example of science being put to practical use is the wealth of **technology** from the space program. It has **applications** in the areas of safety, health, and even **recreation**.

Because of the danger of radiation and temperature extremes in space, you as a **consumer** may now benefit from sunglasses that block out the sun's harmful rays. You may also **savor** fresh food products **encased** in aluminum-coated plastic to protect them from heat and cold. Or you may enjoy the comfort provided by similar aluminized insulation that reflects energy in your home.

The challenge of putting people in space has also resulted in the development of home water **purifiers** that reduce lead, odors, and other **pollutants**. In addition, computers used in aircraft design have led to "virtual reality." This computer-assisted **video** system places you into an imaginary environment with the sense of actually being there.

You can see that space spinoffs certainly have the **potential** of going far beyond powdered orange juice and freeze-dried food!

DO YOU READ ME?

What is the main idea of this selection?

Check the best answer.

○ Aluminum keeps you warm.

○ Sunglasses block out rays.

○ We get many new products from the space program.

○ We learn about space.

ALPHABET SHOWS WORD ORDER

Write the New Words in alphabetical order.

1. _____

2. _____

3. _____

4. _____

5. _____

6. _____

7. _____

8. _____

9. _____

10. _____

LINK FOUND BETWEEN WORDS AND MEANINGS

Use context clues to match each New Word with its meaning. Write the correct letter on each line.

____ 1. technology

____ 2. applications

____ 3. recreation

____ 4. consumer

____ 5. encased

____ 6. savor

____ 7. purifiers

____ 8. pollutants

____ 9. video

____ 10. potential

a. enclosed or surrounded

b. ways of being put to use

c. a quality capable of being developed; possibility

d. enjoyable pastime; any form of amusement or relaxation

e. things that eliminate dirt or impurities

f. one who buys and uses

g. to enjoy a pleasing sensation

h. things that add dirt or impurities

i. the use of scientific discoveries for practical purposes

j. relating to the sending or receiving of images on a television or other electronic screen

COMPLETED SENTENCES MAKE MEANING CLEAR

Use the New Words to finish these sentences.

1. For desert we had ice cream _____ in a rich chocolate cake.

2. I ate slowly, so I could _____ the sweet taste.

3. We must constantly be learning how to use new _____ .

4. In some cases, a new invention has many _____ .

5. My brother is saving money to buy a new _____ game.

6. He has been a _____ of these games since he began receiving an allowance.

7. Technology has helped to give us more time for _____ .

8. It has the _____ of improving our lives in many areas.

9. All the faucets in our house are equipped with water _____ .

10. My family is concerned about all the _____ in the environment.

SYNONYMS ARE CLOSELY RELATED

☞ **Synonyms** are words with nearly the same meaning.

dish and **plate**

sofa and **couch**

Find a synonym from the list that replaces the word in parentheses in each sentence. Write the synonyms on the lines.

Word List

exceptional

permit

muscular

expression

entire

humorous

nasty

shatter

1. Jeremy ate the _____ pizza by himself.
   (whole)

2. Everyone enjoyed reading Juan's _____ story.
   (funny)

3. The startled _____ on her face caused us to laugh.
   (look)

4. This vase will _____ if it is dropped.
   (break)

5. Christina has _____ talent in music and art.
   (wonderful)

6. My father's legs are _____ because he runs every day.
   (strong)

7. The dog's _____ growl caused me to turn and run.
   (mean)

8. My mother does not _____ me to stay up late on week nights.
   (let)

RIDDLE BRINGS NEW TECHNOLOGY TO LIGHT

Use words from the Word List to solve the puzzle. The answer to the riddle is in the shaded column.

Riddle: Without this, you would be in the dark.

Word List

savor

recreation

technology

applications

encased

pollutants

consumer

video

challenge

energy

CLUES

1. ways of putting things to use _ _ _ _ _ _ _ _ _ _ _ _

2. enjoyable pastimes _ _ _ _ _ _ _ _ _ _

3. one who buys and uses _ _ _ _ _ _ _ _

4. the use of scientific discoveries for practical purposes _ _ _ _ _ _ _ _ _ _

5. enclosed or surrounded _ _ _ _ _ _ _

6. to enjoy a pleasing sensation _ _ _ _ _

7. materials that add dirt or impurities _ _ _ _ _ _ _ _ _ _

8. having to do with television images _ _ _ _ _

9. a demand for best effort _ _ _ _ _ _ _ _ _

10. a force able to do work _ _ _ _ _ _

LOST IN SPACE

Imagine you were on a space expedition and became lost in space. Write an article about your experience. These questions will help guide your writing:

- What do you see in space?
- How does it feel to be lost in space?
- What does Earth look like from where you are?

Use at least four New Words in your article.

FIND OUT MORE ABOUT THE SPACE PROGRAM

BOOKS:

- *Spinoff 93* by NASA. (U.S. Government Printing Office, 1993)

- *The Astronaut Training Book for Kids* by Kim Long. (Lodestar Books, 1990)

CD ROM:

- *Space Shuttle*. (Cambridge Science, 1994)

Don't space out. Take the test!

SPACE NEWS You may be wearing athletic shoes made of space-age fibers that were first used for cushioning and ventilation in Apollo lunar suits!

TEST-DAY TIPS TOLD

On test day bring your own eraser and make sure it erases cleanly.

Complete each definition with the best word. Fill in the circle for the answer at the bottom of the page.

1 Ways of using things are called . . . .

    A purifiers   **C** pollutants
    B applications   **D** recreation

2 Having to do with television is the meaning of . . . .

    A technology   **C** potential
    B applications   **D** video

3 An activity that refreshes one's body and mind, especially after work, is called . . . .

    A applications   **C** technology
    B recreation   **D** purifiers

4 Machines and other devices that clean air and water are called . . . .

    A potential   **C** pollutants
    B technology   **D** purifiers

5 To be completely surrounded by something is to be . . . .

    A potential   **C** technology
    B encased   **D** pollutants

6 Power or skill that may be developed in the future is called . . . .

    A potential   **C** recreation
    B technology   **D** applications

7 Harmful chemicals or wastes that get into the water or air are called . . . .

    A technology   **C** pollutants
    B applications   **D** potential

8 To taste with enjoyment is to . . . .

    A savor   **C** potential
    B video   **D** encased

Read the paragraph. Select the words that best fit in the blanks. Fill in the circles for the answers at the bottom of the page.

It is important to our environment that each one of us becomes an intelligent __9__ . __10__ has developed thousands of new products for us to use, and there is great __11__ for better and more exciting ones in the future. However, we must always weigh the benefits of these inventions against the harm that possible __12__ may add to the environment.

9   **A** video   **C** consumer
    B potential   **D** technology

10 **A** Video   **C** Recreation
    B Consumer   **D** Technology

11 **A** potential   **C** consumer
    B recreation   **D** applications

12 **A** technology   **C** recreation
    B potential   **D** pollutants

ANSWERS

1	Ⓐ Ⓑ Ⓒ Ⓓ	4	Ⓐ Ⓑ Ⓒ Ⓓ	7	Ⓐ Ⓑ Ⓒ Ⓓ	10	Ⓐ Ⓑ Ⓒ Ⓓ
2	Ⓐ Ⓑ Ⓒ Ⓓ	5	Ⓐ Ⓑ Ⓒ Ⓓ	8	Ⓐ Ⓑ Ⓒ Ⓓ	11	Ⓐ Ⓑ Ⓒ Ⓓ
3	Ⓐ Ⓑ Ⓒ Ⓓ	6	Ⓐ Ⓑ Ⓒ Ⓓ	9	Ⓐ Ⓑ Ⓒ Ⓓ	12	Ⓐ Ⓑ Ⓒ Ⓓ

REMEDY FOR HICCUPS STILL A MYSTERY

Does this sound **familiar**? You're about to say something when suddenly... HIC! You **hiccup**. Your friends begin to giggle. HIC! You try to stop. HIC! But you can't. HIC!

What causes hiccups? A signal from the brain races to your **spinal cord**, a thick bundle of nerves inside your spine, or backbone. A nerve in the spinal cord sends out another signal that causes a **spasm** of your **diaphragm**. The diaphragm is a large, powerful muscle across the base of your chest **cavity**. It contracts and relaxes when you breathe. Normally the **contractions** are **rhythmic** and gentle, but the spasm makes your diaphragm contract in jerks. It makes you **abruptly** take in a big gulp of air. At that same moment your throat closes. The air bumps against your closed throat; the result is hiccupping.

How do you stop hiccupping? One way is by shocking your diaphragm out of its contractions. Here are some **remedies** to try:

let someone frighten you;
eat a spoonful of crushed ice;
hold your breath;
suck on a lemon;
breathe into a paper bag;
stand on your head and breathe through your nose.

MAIN IDEA FOUND IN STORY

What does this story mainly show?
Check the best answer.

○ what causes hiccups
○ what is the best remedy for hiccups
○ why people laugh when you hiccup
○ what happens in your body when you hiccup

ALPHABET PUTS WORDS IN ORDER

NEW WORDS

Write the New Words in alphabetical order.

familiar

rhythmic

hiccup

spinal cord

spasm

diaphragm

cavity

contractions

abruptly

remedies

1. _____

2. _____

3. _____

4. _____

5. _____

6. _____

7. _____

8. _____

9. _____

10. _____

WORDS AND MEANINGS — A PERFECT MATCH

Use context clues to match each New Word with its meaning.
Write the correct letter on each line.

____ 1. familiar

____ 2. rhythmic

____ 3. hiccup

____ 4. spinal cord

____ 5. spasm

____ 6. diaphragm

____ 7. cavity

____ 8. contractions

____ 9. abruptly

____ 10. remedies

a. cures or solutions

b. well-known; recognizable

c. the shortening or pulling inward of muscles

d. occurring at regular intervals

e. a hole or open area

f. to inhale abruptly from an involuntary contraction of the diaphragm, producing a sharp sound

g. a large muscle at the base of the chest area, used for breathing

h. a thick bundle of nerves running through the backbone

i. a sudden, involuntary muscle tightening

j. suddenly; without warning

WORDS FILL INCOMPLETE SENTENCES

Use the New Words to finish these sentences.

1. My sister ate her dinner too fast and began to _____ .

2. The strong _____ of her diaphragm were painful.

3. In my dream, I was walking through a neighborhood that did not look _____.

4. The steady _____ sound of my mother knocking on my bedroom door woke me up.

5. The dentist said my pain was caused by a _____ in my tooth.

6. Nerves in your _____ send signals to the brain from various parts of the body.

7. My uncle sometimes gets a muscle _____ in his leg at night.

8. After his recent illness, the doctor told him to do breathing exercises to strengthen his _____ .

9. As we passed the bookstore, my mother stopped the car _____ .

10. She wanted to buy a book about old-fashioned folk _____ .

 # OPPOSITES ATTRACT

👉 **Antonyms** are words that have opposite meanings.

beginning and **end**   **quiet** and **loud**

Use the Word List to find the antonyms for these words. Write the correct words on the lines.

Word List

strange

gradually

expansions

informed

minor

positive

artificial

smooth

sell

minimum

1. major _____

2. familiar _____

3. maximum _____

4. abruptly _____

5. coarse _____

6. contractions _____

7. negative _____

8. ignorant _____

9. real _____

10. purchase _____

SEARCH IS ON FOR HIDDEN WORDS

Find the New Words in the puzzle. The words may appear vertically, horizontally, diagonally, or from bottom to top.

New Words

familiar

rhythmic

hiccup

spinal cord

spasm

diaphragm

cavity

contractions

abruptly

remedies

```
F A M I L I A R S P X O R
H B D H I C H I N G H T H
I R R V E A T S O U I T Y
C U A B A V E G I L F I T
C P A P S I S C T M R R H
U T A P U T C U C G E D M
P L G H I Y O R A A M H I
T Y N L T D N R R E K C
S A U K M I S E T H D B M
L T E S B P I N N P I O P
X E A M L A S T O A E Y S
C P O N E S T S C I S S E
S P I N A L C O R D Y G D
```

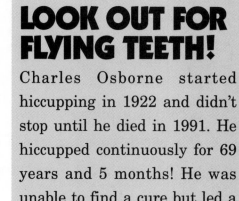

LOOK OUT FOR FLYING TEETH!

Charles Osborne started hiccupping in 1922 and didn't stop until he died in 1991. He hiccupped continuously for 69 years and 5 months! He was unable to find a cure but led a reasonably normal life. He did admit, however, that he couldn't keep his false teeth in.

FIND OUT MORE ABOUT YOUR BODY

READ:

- *All About Digestion* by Donna Bailey. (Steck Vaughn, 1991)
- *The Brain and Nervous System* by Steve Parker. (Franklin Watts, 1990)
- *Outside and Inside Your Body* by Sandra Markle. (Bradbury Press, 1991)
- *The Magic School Bus Inside the Human Body* by Joanna Cole. (Scholastic, 1989)
- *You Can't Sneeze with Your Eyes Open & Other Freaky Facts About the Human Body* by Barbara Seuling. (Dutton, 1986)

WHAT'S YOUR EXCUSE?

 Write five sentences trying to persuade your classmates to maintain healthy bodies.

These questions will help guide your writing:

- Why is it important to have a healthy body?
- Why are good eating habits important for a healthy body?
- What types of activites and exercises help maintain a healthy body?

Use at least four New Words in your writing.

Take a big gulp and go for the test!

IMPROVE YOUR SCORE

If you skip a question in the test, be sure to skip that line in the answer box.

Read each group of words. Select the word or words that mean the __same__ as the underlined word. Fill in the circle for the answer at the bottom of the page.

1 move <u>abruptly</u>

- **A** often
- **B** seldom
- **C** suddenly
- **D** slowly

2 contract the <u>diaphragm</u>

- **A** dish
- **B** curtain
- **C** muscle
- **D** ground

3 a <u>familiar</u> sight

- **A** terrible
- **B** well-known
- **C** lovely
- **D** colorful

4 hurt the <u>spinal cord</u>

- **A** nerve tissue
- **B** digestive system
- **C** muscle
- **D** skeleton

5 inside the chest <u>cavity</u>

- **A** space in the body
- **B** solid place
- **C** toothache
- **D** sharp pain

6 <u>hiccup</u> loudly

- **A** cough
- **B** giggle
- **C** moan and groan
- **D** gulp air abruptly

7 <u>rhythmic</u> beat

- **A** patterned
- **B** strong
- **C** noisy
- **D** slow

8 <u>remedies</u> for the problems

- **A** chances
- **B** penalties
- **C** solutions
- **D** offers

Read each set of sentences. Select the word that best completes the second sentence in each set. Fill in the circle for the answer at the bottom of the page.

9 The <u>rhythmic</u> sound of the waves washing the shore put me to sleep.
Rhythmic means—

- **A** loud
- **B** regular
- **C** soft
- **D** pounding

10 The pain was caused by a <u>spasm</u> in his back.
Spasm means—

- **A** blow
- **B** tightening
- **C** stab
- **D** wound

11 He has tried at least ten <u>remedies</u> for his hiccups.
Remedies means—

- **A** causes
- **B** reasons
- **C** exercises
- **D** cures

12 I can actually feel the <u>contractions</u> in the muscle.
Contractions means acts of getting—

- **A** smoother
- **B** stronger
- **C** smaller
- **D** weaker

ANSWERS

1	Ⓐ Ⓑ Ⓒ Ⓓ	4	Ⓐ Ⓑ Ⓒ Ⓓ	7	Ⓐ Ⓑ Ⓒ Ⓓ	10	Ⓐ Ⓑ Ⓒ Ⓓ
2	Ⓐ Ⓑ Ⓒ Ⓓ	5	Ⓐ Ⓑ Ⓒ Ⓓ	8	Ⓐ Ⓑ Ⓒ Ⓓ	11	Ⓐ Ⓑ Ⓒ Ⓓ
3	Ⓐ Ⓑ Ⓒ Ⓓ	6	Ⓐ Ⓑ Ⓒ Ⓓ	9	Ⓐ Ⓑ Ⓒ Ⓓ	12	Ⓐ Ⓑ Ⓒ Ⓓ

TONI MORRISON — NOBEL PRIZE WINNER

As a little girl, Toni Morrison liked to listen to her parents tell stories of their **childhood**. These stories gave her a love for storytelling and reading. That's why when she went to college, she studied **journalism**. In 1953, Toni received her degree and **graduated** from Howard University in Washington, D.C.

After college, Toni became an editor at a **publishing** company in New York where she was able to help many young African American writers get their books published. But it was her own writing that **established** Toni as a **distinguished** person in American **literature**. The African American **folklore** of her childhood **inspires** her writing. She tells stories that reflect both the pain and beauty of African Americans' experiences.

Beloved, her fifth novel, won the Pulitzer Prize for Literature in 1988. In 1993, Toni received another great honor, the **Nobel Prize** in Literature. She is the second American woman and the first African American woman to receive this award.

ONE THING LEADS TO ANOTHER

Which happened last?

Check the best answer.

❑ Toni graduated from Howard University.

❑ Toni won the Nobel Prize.

❑ Toni studied journalism.

❑ Toni listened to her parents' stories.

THE AMAZING ALPHABET

Write the New Words in alphabetical order.

New Words

childhood

inspires

publishing

established

graduated

distinguished

literature

folklore

journalism

Nobel Prize

1. _____

2. _____

3. _____

4. _____

5. _____

6. _____

7. _____

8. _____

9. _____

10. _____

WORDS AND MEANINGS — A PRIZE-WINNING MATCH

Use context clues to match each New Word with its meaning. Write the correct letter on each line.

____ 1. childhood

____ 2. journalism

____ 3. publishing

____ 4. established

____ 5. graduated

____ 6. distinguished

____ 7. literature

____ 8. folklore

____ 9. inspires

____ 10. Nobel Prize

a. the condition or time of being young, not adult

b. a prize given once a year for excellence in the sciences or literature or for promoting peace

c. the collection and presentation of news

d. traditional customs, sayings, and stories of a people

e. making and selling books

f. writing of great and lasting value

g. caused to be; set up

h. known for being excellent; celebrated

i. received an academic degree or diploma

j. influences or motivates by example

24

NEW WORDS FINISH SENTENCES

Use the New Words to finish these sentences.

1. Some people decide on a career during their _____ .

2. My sister knew she wanted to work in television _____ from a very early age.

3. My brother has always loved books, so he wants to be in the _____ business.

4. My father _____ from law school ten years ago.

5. He _____ his own business after several years.

6. People call my grandfather a _____ professor of English.

7. He enjoys teaching his students about language and _____ .

8. I love learning about the customs and _____ of people from other parts of the world.

9. Studying folklore _____ me to write my own stories.

10. Maybe someday I will win a _____ for my work.

SUFFIXES GIVE WORDS HAPPY ENDINGS

☞ A **suffix** is a word part that can be added to the end of a root word. Adding a suffix changes the meaning of the root word.

The suffix **ive** means <u>having to do with</u>, or <u>likely to</u>.

Add the suffix <u>ive</u> to the underlined words below. Write the new words on the lines. You may need to change the spelling of some of the words.

MEANING	NEW WORD
1. having to do with <u>investigation</u>	_____
2. likely to <u>aggress</u>	_____
3. having to do with <u>description</u>	_____
4. likely to <u>support</u>	_____
5. likely to <u>persuade</u>	_____
6. having to do with <u>narration</u>	_____
7. likely to <u>act</u>	_____
8. likely to <u>explode</u>	_____
9. having to do with <u>expense</u>	_____

Check the dictionary if you need help.

25

BIG BRAINSTORM HEADED THIS WAY!

Under each heading below, write down as many ideas as you can. Then go back and review your lists.

people you admire

_____
_____
_____

careers that interest you

_____
_____
_____

favorite authors

_____
_____
_____
_____

problems you have overcome

_____
_____
_____
_____

awards you would like to win

_____
_____
_____
_____

favorite types of literature

_____
_____
_____

DO YOU LOVE BOOKS AS MUCH AS TONI MORRISON DOES?

Read:

- *Extraordinary Black Americans from Colonial to Contemporary Times* by Susan Altman. (Childrens Press, 1989)

TALES BY TONI

Some books written by Toni Morrison include the following: *Song of Solomon* (1977), *Tar Baby* (1981), *Beloved* (1988), *Playing in the Dark* (1992), and *Jazz* (1992).

KEEP YOUR EYES ON THE PRIZE

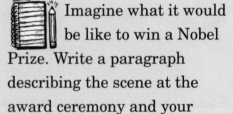 Imagine what it would be like to win a Nobel Prize. Write a paragraph describing the scene at the award ceremony and your feelings about it.

These questions will help guide your writing:

- What did you win the award for?
- What famous people are there to watch you accept your award?
- How does it feel to win such a great award?

Use at least four New Words in your writing.

Read on to the test!

SECRETS TO SUCCESS ON TESTS

Mark your answers with a sharpened, no. 2 pencil. Have several handy in case one breaks.

Complete each definition with the best word or words. Fill in the circle for the answer at the bottom of the page.

1 To have <u>graduated</u> is to have—

   A gone on a vacation
   B received a diploma
   C received a grade
   D just started school

2 To be <u>distinguished</u> is to be—

   A unknown
   B far away
   C famous
   D responsible

3 To study <u>literature</u> is to study—

   A geography
   B mathematics
   C geometry
   D writings

4 If you <u>established</u> something, you—

   A destroyed it
   B finished it
   C brought it into being
   D wrote it

5 The field of <u>journalism</u> refers to—

   A reporting the news
   B keeping a diary
   C farming the land
   D drawing pictures

6 If something <u>inspires</u>, it—

   A fixes
   B repairs
   C perspires
   D influences

Read each sentence. Select the answer that best completes the sentence. Fill in the circle for the answer at the bottom of the page.

7 The things you learn in your ____ will influence you for the rest of your life.

   A folklore
   B childhood
   C literature
   D journalism

8 What ____ company is responsible for these books?

   A distinguished
   B literature
   C publishing
   D journalism

9 The story "Jack and the Beanstalk" is a part of the ____ of England and America.

   A publishing
   B journalism
   C childhood
   D folklore

10 Each year, the ____ is awarded to people who have done great things.

   A literature
   B Nobel Prize
   C journalism
   D folklore

11 Babe Ruth is one of the most ____ players of the game of baseball.

   A established
   B distinguished
   C folklore
   D graduated

12 Toni Morrison is especially interested in creating ____ about the lives of African Americans.

   A journalism
   B literature
   C childhood
   D publishing

ANSWERS

1	Ⓐ Ⓑ Ⓒ Ⓓ	4	Ⓐ Ⓑ Ⓒ Ⓓ	7	Ⓐ Ⓑ Ⓒ Ⓓ	10	Ⓐ Ⓑ Ⓒ Ⓓ
2	Ⓐ Ⓑ Ⓒ Ⓓ	5	Ⓐ Ⓑ Ⓒ Ⓓ	8	Ⓐ Ⓑ Ⓒ Ⓓ	11	Ⓐ Ⓑ Ⓒ Ⓓ
3	Ⓐ Ⓑ Ⓒ Ⓓ	6	Ⓐ Ⓑ Ⓒ Ⓓ	9	Ⓐ Ⓑ Ⓒ Ⓓ	12	Ⓐ Ⓑ Ⓒ Ⓓ

MOUNTAIN BIKERS CONQUER THE EARTH

W hat offers the thrill of **competitive** racing, as well as the tranquility of riding alone through uncharted wilderness? Mountain biking has just this!

By definition, "mountain biking" suggests a cycling sport not confined to the pavement. A few mechanical **alterations** allow the bike to **maneuver** on varied land surfaces. Then bikers are ready to master almost any **terrain.**

The first off-road, down-hill bike race was held in California. The bikers used **refurbished** bikes with coaster brakes. Soon, a new type of bike was **built**, better suited to the demands of cycling down a mountain. Today mountain bikes sport lightweight frames, handlebar shifters, numerous gear speeds, and strong **suspensions** to absorb the shock of jolting downhill.

The practice, training, and **endurance** needed to compete in mountain biking may **intimidate** you. But with sound equipment, balance, and **coordination**, anyone can enjoy mountain biking!

READERS PICK BEST TITLE

What is the best title for this story?

Check the best answer.

_____ Why Bikes Have Shocks

_____ What Is Mountain Biking?

_____ How to Make Mountain Bikes

_____ Where to Mountain Bike

ALPHABET KEEPS WORDS IN ORDER

NEW WORDS

competitive
alterations
maneuver
terrain
refurbished
built
suspensions
endurance
intimidate
coordination

Write the New Words in alphabetical order.

1. _____

2. _____

3. _____

4. _____

5. _____

6. _____

7. _____

8. _____

9. _____

10. _____

WORDS AND MEANINGS—A PERFECT MATCH

Use context clues to match each New Word with its meaning. Write the correct letter on each line.

____ 1. endurance

____ 2. alterations

____ 3. terrain

____ 4. refurbished

____ 5. competitive

____ 6. built

____ 7. suspensions

____ 8. maneuver

____ 9. intimidate

____ 10. coordination

a. constructed; made

b. related to competition; driven to compete

c. to dominate or frighten

d. changes or modifications

e. strength; ability to last

f. to make a series of changes in direction or position

g. supporting frameworks

h. a piece of land with particular features

i. renovated; freshened up

j. the ability to act together in a smooth way

INCOMPLETE SENTENCES NEED HELP FROM NEW WORDS

Use New Words to finish these sentences.

1. The idea of competing in a race can _____ some people.

2. Training develops _____ so that muscles work together smoothly.

3. The army tested a new vehicle to see how it would _____ .

4. They drove it over many different kinds of _____ , and it always performed well.

5. Some athletes are so _____ that they will do anything to win.

6. They will spend huge sums of money making _____ in their equipment to give themselves an advantage.

7. My aunt and uncle bought a _____ farmhouse.

8. They also _____ a small studio apartment in the backyard for guests.

9. Those motorcycles have stronger _____ than usual.

10. It takes _____ to compete in a long motorcycle race.

DRAWING THE LINE WITH SYNONYMS

☞ **Synonyms** are words with nearly the same meaning.

| start and begin | friend and pal |

Draw a line to match each pair of synonyms below.

1. strength	a. endurance	11. jealousy	a. clumsy
2. made	b. built	12. purpose	b. grin
3. threaten	c. intimidate	13. awkward	c. simple
4. amaze	d. annual	14. smile	d. envy
5. yearly	e. astonish	15. easy	e. reason
6. completely	a. journey	16. choose	a. cost
7. sketch	b. imagine	17. reply	b. error
8. leave	c. draw	18. price	c. answer
9. pretend	d. totally	19. mistake	d. trade
10. voyage	e. depart	20. exchange	e. pick

SCRAMBLED WORDS FINALLY SORTED OUT

Unscramble the New Words and write them on the lines.

NEW WORDS

competitive	1. ordocnitanio _____
alterations	2. titevipeomc _____
maneuver	3. dancerune _____
terrain	4. ratoisnetal _____
refurbished	5. lubit _____
built	6. mauveren _____
suspensions	7. drerbufihes _____
endurance	8. reranit _____
intimidate	9. pussnseonis _____
coordination	10. miditintae _____

READERS TELL ABOUT WILD RIDE

 Imagine that you took a long trip on a bicycle. Write a story about your experience.

These questions will help guide your writing:

• Where did you go on your trip?

• Who were you with?

• What exciting things happened on the trip?

Use at least four New Words in your story.

 Bike your way through the test!

BIKING BITS

> "Repack," the oldest mountain biking race in the country, is named after bikers who stop to repack their brakes with grease to keep them from burning up on the steep course.

> Did you know that 9 out of 10 mountain bikes are not used off the road? They are used on the city streets. City bikers like the way they handle potholes, cracks, and curbs!

MORE ABOUT MOUNTAIN BIKING

BOOKS:

• *All Action Mountain Biking* by Bob Allen. (Lerner Publications, 1992)

• *The Bicyclist's Sourcebook* by Michael Leccese and Arlene Plevin. (Woodbine House, 1991)

• *Bicycling Magazine's Complete Guide to Riding and Racing Techniques* by Fred Matheny. (Rodale Press, 1989)

PERIODICALS:

Mountain Bike Action
25233 Anza Dr.
Valencia, CA 91355

TEST YOUR BEST

Read all directions carefully. You may even want to read them a second time to make sure you understand.

Read each group of words. Select the word or words that mean the same as the underlined word. Fill in the circle for the answer at the bottom of the page.

1 made a few <u>alterations</u>

   A suggestions
   B changes
   C corrections
   D additions

2 rough <u>terrain</u>

   A people
   B neighborhood
   C water
   D land

3 a <u>refurbished</u> car

   A fast
   B racing
   C family
   D renovated

4 strong <u>suspensions</u>

   A maneuvers
   B frameworks
   C brakes
   D doubts

5 <u>built</u> a model

   A pictured
   B removed
   C constructed
   D admired

6 ran with <u>endurance</u>

   A skill
   B quickness
   C ability to race
   D ability to last

Read each set of sentences. Select the word or words that best complete the second sentence in each set. Fill in the circle for the answer at the bottom of the page.

7 We had to <u>maneuver</u> through all the toys on the floor.
<u>Maneuver</u> means—

   A move clumsily **C** move slowly
   B move skillfully **D** move quickly

8 A basketball player needs speed and <u>coordination</u> to be a success.
<u>Coordination</u> means—

   A quickness   **C** gracefulness
   B skill   **D** talent

9 I did not like the fact that he tried to <u>intimidate</u> me.
<u>Intimidate</u> means—

   A frighten   **C** mistreat
   B cheat   **D** beat

10 Why do you enjoy <u>competitive</u> sports?
<u>Competitive</u> means involving a—

   A ball   **C** contest
   B team   **D** net

11 The bike required several <u>alterations</u> before we could use it in the race.
<u>Alterations</u> means—

   A practices   **C** riders
   B modifications **D** wheels

12 The <u>terrain</u> on the moon is very different from that on Earth.
<u>Terrain</u> means—

   A amount of rain **C** land
   B amount of wind **D** water

ANSWERS

1	Ⓐ Ⓑ Ⓒ Ⓓ	4	Ⓐ Ⓑ Ⓒ Ⓓ	7	Ⓐ Ⓑ Ⓒ Ⓓ	10	Ⓐ Ⓑ Ⓒ Ⓓ
2	Ⓐ Ⓑ Ⓒ Ⓓ	5	Ⓐ Ⓑ Ⓒ Ⓓ	8	Ⓐ Ⓑ Ⓒ Ⓓ	11	Ⓐ Ⓑ Ⓒ Ⓓ
3	Ⓐ Ⓑ Ⓒ Ⓓ	6	Ⓐ Ⓑ Ⓒ Ⓓ	9	Ⓐ Ⓑ Ⓒ Ⓓ	12	Ⓐ Ⓑ Ⓒ Ⓓ

OUR AUTOMATIC SECURITY SYSTEM —
THE EYES HAVE IT

Do you realize that you're doing something you're not even aware of? In fact, you've probably done it at least once while reading this paragraph. **Blinking** is just something your eyes do automatically.

Your eyes are so important that they are well-protected by your eyelids, eyelashes, and **skull**. Blinking is an important part of the "**security** system" that works to keep your eyes from harm.

One way that blinking protects your eyes is by keeping them moist. Blinking spreads a mixture of water, salt, and **mucus** from the **tear glands** onto your eye. The tear glands **secrete** their **fluid** onto the surface of your eyeballs. Your blinking eyelids automatically spread the fluid over your eyes, washing off dust and killing **germs** that might **irritate** them. Your eyeballs stay moist, and you stay comfortable.

Blinking is so important to your eyes that you can't stop blinking, no matter how you try. Check it out. Try having a "no-blinking contest" with a friend. Stare at each other as long as you can without blinking. Sooner or later, one of you will have to blink. But it just goes to prove that your eyes' security system is always on the job!

THE TRUTH ABOUT BLINKING

Are the following statements true or false?

Circle the best answer.

1. Blinking is automatic.

   True   False

2. Blinking is dangerous.

   True   False

3. Blinking protects your eyes.

   True   False

4. Tear glands put tear gas in your eyes.

   True   False

THE AMAZING ALPHABET

Write the New Words in alphabetical order.

NEW WORDS

blinking

skull

mucus

tear

glands

secrete

fluid

germs

irritate

security

1. _____   6. _____

2. _____   7. _____

3. _____   8. _____

4. _____   9. _____

5. _____   10. _____

WORDS AND MEANINGS GO TOGETHER

Use context clues to match each New Word with its meaning.

Write the correct letter on each line.

____ 1. germs

____ 2. blinking

____ 3. mucus

____ 4. secrete

____ 5. tear

____ 6. glands

____ 7. fluid

____ 8. irritate

____ 9. skull

____ 10. security

a. safety from harm

b. rapid automatic opening and shutting of the eye

c. microscopic organisms that cause disease

d. the bones of the head

e. a flowing liquid or gas

f. a thick secretion of the body that moistens and protects

g. to form and give off

h. a clear salty fluid secreted by glands in the eyes

i. body organs that produce and secrete bodily fluids

j. to make something sore or sensitive

WORDS COMPLETE SENTENCES

Use the New Words to finish these sentences.

1. There was so much dust in the air that I couldn't stop my eyes from _____ .

2. Soon the dust really began to _____ my eyes.

3. As we walked along the dusty road, my _____ glands worked overtime.

4. During the winter, maple trees _____ a lot of sap.

5. This sweet _____ is collected and used to make maple syrup.

6. Some people feel that they have to go to work or school even when they are sick and carrying _____ .

7. For other people's _____ it would be better if they stayed home.

8. Because of a bad cold, I had a lot of _____ in my throat.

9. I had such a bad headache that every bone in my _____ seemed to hurt.

10. When the _____ in my throat became swollen, I knew I had the mumps.

SUFFIXES CHANGE WORD MEANING

☞ A **suffix** is a word part that can be added to the end of a root word to change its meaning. The suffixes **able** and **ible** mean <u>able to</u>, <u>likely to</u>, or <u>worthy of</u>.

Add the suffixes <u>able</u> or <u>ible</u> to the underlined words below. Then use the new words you formed to finish the sentences. You will have to drop the final "e" in some of the words.

1. An answer that is likely to <u>work</u> is a _____ answer.

2. A joke worthy of a <u>laugh</u> is a _____ joke.

3. A tool you are able to <u>use</u> is a _____ tool.

4. A person worthy of <u>love</u> is a _____ person.

5. A muscle that is able to <u>flex</u> is a _____ muscle.

6. Candy you are able to <u>chew</u> is _____ candy.

7. A pet you are able to <u>teach</u> is a _____ pet.

8. A chemical that is likely to <u>combust</u> is a _____ chemical.

Need help? Check out the dictionary.

35

READ:

- *The Eye, Window to the World* by Lael Wertenbaker. (Torstar Books, 1984)
- *Sight* by Ed Catherall. (Silver Burdett, 1981)
- *Why Does My Nose Run? (And Other Questions Kids Ask About Their Bodies)* by Joanne Settel and Nancy Baggett. (Atheneum, 1985)
- *Exploring the Human Body* by Ed Catherall. (Raintree, 1992)

ANALOGIES MAKE MEANINGFUL RELATIONSHIPS

👉 **Analogies** show the relationship between things.

trunk is to **tree** as **stalk** is to **corn**

or

trunk : tree :: stalk : corn

Use words from the word list to finish these analogies.

WORD LIST

tear

germs

skull

security

fluid

1. _____ : brain :: shell : egg

2. _____ : eye :: sap :: tree

3. _____ : water :: solid : iron

4. _____ : sickness :: joke : laughter

5. _____ : safety :: risk : danger

THE EYES HAVE IT

📝 Many animals have different kinds of eyes. Owls, cats, and flies have unusual eyes that help them in different ways. Pick two animals and write a research report about their eyes. You can find information in an encyclopedia or other reference books.

These questions will help guide your writing:

- Are the animals active at night or during the day?
- Can they see things that people can't?
- How are their eyes alike or different?

Use at least four New Words in your report.

KEEP YOUR EYE ON THE BALL

Your eyeballs are about the size and shape of ping-pong balls.

Can you see the test?

WHICH WAY IS UP?

What you see forms into an upside-down picture on the back of your eyeball. A nerve rushes the picture to your brain, which turns the picture right-side up again!

TEST-TAKING SECRETS REVEALED

When you are asked to fill in a blank in a sentence, read the entire sentence first. Then try each of the possible answers to see which one is best.

Complete each definition with the best word. Fill in the circle for the answer at the bottom of the page.

1 To bother or make sore is to . . . .

   A secrete
   B wash
   C prove
   D irritate

2 A thick, protecting substance given off by body membranes is . . . .

   A glands
   B mucus
   C germs
   D fluid

3 The bony frame of the head is called the . . . .

   A skull
   B glands
   C mucus
   D blinking

4 Parts of the body like the liver, kidneys, and thyroid act as . . . .

   A germs
   B skull
   C mucus
   D glands

5 The condition of being safe is . . . .

   A blinking
   B security
   C germs
   D skull

6 Any substance capable of flowing is a . . . .

   A tear
   B mucus
   C fluid
   D skull

Read each sentence. Select the answer that best completes the sentence. Fill in the circle for the answer at the bottom of the page.

7 ____ can occur when dirt is blown into your eyes.

   A Glands
   B Mucus
   C Security
   D Blinking

8 The ____ glands in the eyes keep them moist.

   A mucus
   B tear
   C fluid
   D security

9 Disease is often caused by ____ that can't be seen by the unaided eye.

   A mucus
   B germs
   C glands
   D blinking

10 Glands ____ fluids that the body either uses or gives off as waste.

   A irritate
   B kill
   C secrete
   D protect

11 The bones in the ____ protect the very delicate brain tissue in the head.

   A glands
   B eyelid
   C eyelashes
   D skull

12 The tear glands in the eye produce ____ to help keep it healthy.

   A security
   B mucus
   C germs
   D blinking

ANSWERS

1	Ⓐ Ⓑ Ⓒ Ⓓ	4	Ⓐ Ⓑ Ⓒ Ⓓ	7	Ⓐ Ⓑ Ⓒ Ⓓ	10	Ⓐ Ⓑ Ⓒ Ⓓ
2	Ⓐ Ⓑ Ⓒ Ⓓ	5	Ⓐ Ⓑ Ⓒ Ⓓ	8	Ⓐ Ⓑ Ⓒ Ⓓ	11	Ⓐ Ⓑ Ⓒ Ⓓ
3	Ⓐ Ⓑ Ⓒ Ⓓ	6	Ⓐ Ⓑ Ⓒ Ⓓ	9	Ⓐ Ⓑ Ⓒ Ⓓ	12	Ⓐ Ⓑ Ⓒ Ⓓ

MISUNDERSTOOD MAMMAL
NEEDS OUR HELP

Dracula movies and Halloween have done much to hurt the bat's **image**. Many experts would like us to better understand the bat.

Bats are the only **mammals** that have wings and can fly. Some bats are as small as a thumb, while others spread their wings over five feet! Bats are active at night. During the day, they rest, hanging upside down in trees and caves.

Most bats eat insects, sometimes as many as 3,000 a night! Many of these insects would **annoy** people or harm crops. Some bats eat small animals such as fish and frogs. Some bats find insects or small animals in the dark by making **clicking** sounds and listening to the **echoes**.

Even though bats are important to our **environment**, people are destroying their **populations**. Thousands are killed for food. Many people kill them because they think bats are **pests**. **Insecticides** have poisoned others. Their forest feeding areas and caves have been taken over by humans. Some **species** have already become extinct because of people's misunderstanding. Let's help save the misunderstood bat!

SEQUENCE REVEALED

What does the bat do after it makes a clicking sound?

Check the best answer.

- ❑ finds its prey
- ❑ hangs upside down
- ❑ listens for an echo
- ❑ annoys people

ALPHABET KEEPS WORDS UNDER CONTROL

Write the New Words in alphabetical order.

amount

_____

annual

_____

_____

enviable

_____

inseam

_____

_____

pesky

_____

_____

spectator

NEW WORDS
clicking
mammals
image
annoy
echoes
pests
populations
insecticides
environment
species

WORDS MATCH MEANINGS

Use context clues or the glossary to match each New Word below with its meaning.

Write the correct letter on each line.

____ 1. mammals

____ 2. clicking

____ 3. annoy

____ 4. echoes

____ 5. image

____ 6. insecticides

____ 7. environment

____ 8. populations

____ 9. species

____ 10. pests

a. all the conditions that surround a person, animal, or plant and affect such things as growth and actions

b. poisons used to kill insects

c. a general impression of what a person or thing is

d. warm-blooded animals with glands in the female that produce milk for feeding its young

e. groups of people or animals living in a certain area or place

f. to irritate, bother, or make slightly angry

g. persons or things that cause trouble, especially insects or small animals that destroy things

h. making or causing a light tapping

i. sounds heard when sound waves bounce back from a surface

j. a group of plants or animals that are alike in certain ways

NEW WORDS CLICK WITH INCOMPLETE SENTENCES

Finish these sentences. Write a New Word on each line.

NEW WORDS

image

annoy

echoes

populations

insecticides

mammals

clicking

environment

pests

species

1. Loud music can _____ some people.
2. They would much rather have a quiet _____ .
3. The camera was _____ again and again.
4. The photographer wanted to capture a favorable _____ in the picture.
5. _____ are meant to kill certain bugs.
6. Unfortunately, they may kill some _____ as well.
7. You could hear the _____ from the mountainside.
8. Huge _____ of people could hear them.
9. Most people think all insects are _____ .
10. However, only a few of the over seven hundred thousand _____ are harmful to people.

PREFIXES CREATE A WHOLE NEW MEANING

☞ A **prefix** is a word part that can be added to the beginning of a root word. Adding a prefix changes the meaning of the root word.

The prefix **sub** can mean:

1. under
2. not quite, somewhat
3. part of a whole

The prefix **super** can mean:

1. over or above; on top of
2. very much; more than normal
3. greater than others

Look at each meaning. Write the word by adding the prefix <u>sub</u> or <u>super</u> to the underlined root word.

MEANING

1. part of a whole <u>species</u>
2. greater than other <u>markets</u>
3. on top of another <u>structure</u>
4. under the <u>soil</u>
5. not quite <u>normal</u>

PREFIX + ROOT WORD

1. _____
2. _____
3. _____
4. _____
5. _____

PUZZLING BEHAVIOR

Use the New Words to complete the crossword puzzle.

ACROSS

1. Study these _____ of animals.
4. The _____ are declining.
6. hear the _____
8. a cold _____
10. will _____ the sleeping baby

DOWN

2. improved her _____
3. sprayed the _____ over the crops
5. is _____ her fingers
7. Flies are _____ .
9. _____ are warm-blooded.

THE TRUTH ABOUT BATS

The bumblebee bat is the world's smallest mammal—it is only one inch long. The flying fox bat, on the other hand, can have a wing span of as much as five feet.

PLEASE DON'T HARM THE BATS

 Write a paragraph telling what you would say to convince people not to harm bats. Share your paragraph with a friend.

The following questions will help guide your writing:

- How are bats important to our environment?
- In what ways are bats being harmed?
- What will happen to the bats if they are not protected?

Use at least four New Words in your paragraph.

READ MORE ABOUT IT

- *Bats: The Night Fliers* by Anabel Dean. (Lerner, 1974)
- *Bats* by M. Brock Fenton. (Facts on File, 1974)
- *Eyewitness Juniors: Amazing Bats* by Frank Greenway. (Dorling Kindersley Education, 1991)
- *Bats: Creatures of the Night* by Joyce Milton. (Grosset and Dunlap, 1993)
- *Extremely Weird Bats* by Sarah Lovett. (J. Muir Publications, 1991)

Don't take the test in the dark!

SCORE HIGHER ON TESTS

Look at all possible answers. Leave out the ones that you are sure are incorrect. Decide which of the remaining answers is better or best.

Read each group of words. Select the word or words that mean the <u>same</u> as the underlined word. Fill in the circle for the answer at the bottom of the page.

1 a good <u>image</u>

   A impression
   B discussion
   C idea
   D game

2 <u>annoy</u> my brother

   A greet
   B bother
   C help
   D tell

3 heard the <u>clicking</u>

   A scraping sounds
   B loud noises
   C soft whispers
   D sharp sounds

4 get rid of <u>pests</u>

   A animals
   B dogs
   C cats
   D troublemakers

5 spray the <u>insecticides</u>

   A clean fluids
   B paints
   C poisons
   D insects

6 name of the <u>species</u>

   A group of stores
   B group of animals
       or plants
   C group of families
   D group of schools

Read each sentence. Select the word that best completes each one. Fill in the circle for the answer at the bottom of the page.

7 Bears are _____ that sleep for long periods of time.

   A populations   **C** pests
   B mammals   **D** insecticides

8 The _____ could be heard as the sounds bounced off the walls of the canyon.

   A mammals   **C** echoes
   B populations   **D** pests

9 Your _____ is all that is around you.

   A species   **C** environment
   B image   **D** populations

10 _____ of bats gather underneath the bridge.

   A Populations   **C** Mammals
   B Pests   **D** Echoes

11 We will use _____ to get rid of the unwanted ants.

   A echoes   **C** species
   B insecticides **D** pests

12 He spent a lot of time trying to improve his _____.

   A populations   **C** pests
   B species   **D** image

ANSWERS

1	Ⓐ Ⓑ Ⓒ Ⓓ	4	Ⓐ Ⓑ Ⓒ Ⓓ	7	Ⓐ Ⓑ Ⓒ Ⓓ	10	Ⓐ Ⓑ Ⓒ Ⓓ
2	Ⓐ Ⓑ Ⓒ Ⓓ	5	Ⓐ Ⓑ Ⓒ Ⓓ	8	Ⓐ Ⓑ Ⓒ Ⓓ	11	Ⓐ Ⓑ Ⓒ Ⓓ
3	Ⓐ Ⓑ Ⓒ Ⓓ	6	Ⓐ Ⓑ Ⓒ Ⓓ	9	Ⓐ Ⓑ Ⓒ Ⓓ	12	Ⓐ Ⓑ Ⓒ Ⓓ

GET A KICK
OUT OF THE MARTIAL ARTS

What are the **martial arts** really all about? The martial arts were first developed for **self-defense**. According to Ernie Reyes, star of TV's "Sidekicks", "The idea isn't to go out and fight. Martial arts isn't just **boisterous** kicking and punching. It's discipline and **respect**."

There are many kinds of martial arts. Karate involves delivering focused attacks with parts of the body such as feet, hands, knees, and elbows. In judo, students are taught how to harness the body's energy in the most efficient way. They learn how to unbalance an attacker or an **intruder** so that he or she can be controlled. The student of aikido learns to use circular movements and wrist and arm techniques to control a **threatening** opponent.

Some think that martial artists are very **aggressive**. As it turns out, just the opposite is often true. Most martial artists are like Ernie Reyes—quiet, **conscientious**, and **industrious**, with high self-esteem. Violence is not what they're all about. So, the next time you're looking to boost your **confidence** and flex your muscles, try out the martial arts. One of them might just be the kick you're looking for.

WHAT'S YOUR OPINION?

Are these sentences fact or opinion? *Write an F if the sentence is a fact or an O if it is an opinion.*

_____ 1. Ernie Reyes is a great actor.

_____ 2. There are many kinds of martial arts.

_____ 3. Judo is the most challenging of the martial arts.

_____ 4. Ernie Reyes is the star of a TV show.

New Words

martial arts
respect
boisterous
intruder
threatening
aggressive
conscientious
industrious
self-defense
confidence

ALPHABET BUILDS WORD ORDER

Write the New Words in alphabetical order.

adapt

_____

_____

combination

_____

_____

count

_____

join

_____

_____

seldom

_____

_____

WORDS AND MEANINGS – A PERFECT MATCH

Use context clues to match each New Word with its meaning. Write the correct letter on each line.

____ 1. martial arts

____ 2. respect

____ 3. boisterous

____ 4. intruder

____ 5. threatening

____ 6. aggressive

____ 7. conscientious

____ 8. industrious

____ 9. self-defense

____ 10. confidence

a. belief in one's own powers and abilities

b. the various systems of self-defense

c. hard-working; busy

d. loud; rude; ill-mannered

e. careful; showing great attention to detail; honest

f. giving signs of an intent to do harm

g. protection of oneself

h. high regard; esteem

i. unwanted visitor

j. inclined to start quarrels or fight; actively bold

NEW WORDS ZERO IN ON SENTENCE HOLES

Use the New Words to finish these sentences.

The clues below the lines will help you choose the best New Word.

I became _____ last year and started taking _____ . I wanted people's
          hard-working   judo, for example

_____ for my skill as a fighter. Sometimes I was afraid being around
     honor

_____ older kids. I also felt that I could protect my family from an
     loud

_____ . One day a strange person began _____ me on the street.
   trespasser   scaring

He seemed very _____ , and I thought he might attack me. I had been
                offensive

_____ in practicing my fighting skills, so in _____ , I got ready to
 attention to detail   protecting self

confront the person. In the end, I didn't need to use my skills. My _____ made the
                                           self-assurance

hostile person go away.

SUFFIXES CHANGE WORD MEANINGS

A **suffix** is a word part that can be added to the end of a root word to change the meaning of the word.

The suffix **ment** can mean <u>the act of</u>, <u>the result of</u>, or <u>the state of</u>.

Add the suffix <u>ment</u> to each underlined word below, and write the new word on the line.

MEANING	ROOT WORD + SUFFIX
1. state of being <u>excited</u>	_____
2. result of <u>agreeing</u>	_____
3. act of <u>enjoying</u>	_____
4. state of being <u>amazed</u>	_____
5. act of <u>developing</u>	_____
6. act of <u>assigning</u>	_____

RIDDLE REVEALS MYSTERIOUS ARTIST

Use New Words to finish the puzzle. The answer to the riddle appears in the shaded column.

Riddle: Who do many people believe was the greatest martial artist of them all?

Clues

New Words

martial arts
respect
boisterous
intruder
threatening
aggressive
conscientious
industrious
self-defense
confidence

1. loud and rude

2. hard-working

3. unwanted visitor
4. belief in one's own powers and abilities
5. high regard or esteem

6. protection of oneself
7. giving signs of an intent to do harm

8. inclined to fight

THE STORY OF A CHAMPION

Imagine you are a world champion martial artist. Write a paragraph telling about how you became the best in the world.

These questions will help guide your writing:

- Who was your teacher?
- How many years did you take lessons?
- What was your toughest competition?

Use at least four New Words in your paragraph.

GET A KICK
OUT OF THESE FACTS!

Guess who was inside Donatello's turtle suit in the first *Teenage Mutant Ninja Turtles* movie? It was none other than Ernie Reyes! While wearing his heavy latex turtle suit during filming in the hot North Carolina summer, Reyes sweated off four pounds a day!

LEARN MORE ABOUT MARTIAL ARTS

- *Martial Arts for Young Athletes* by Michael DePasquale. (Wanderer Books, 1984)
- *Junior Martial Arts* by Tony Gummerson. (A. & C. Books, 1990)

Be a champion. Take the test.

TEST-DAY TIPS TOLD

Never leave an answer blank. Think about the question and make your very best guess.

Read each group of words. Select the word or words that mean the <u>opposite</u> of the underlined word. Fill in the circle for the answer at the bottom of the page.

1 an <u>aggressive</u> player

   A threatening   **C** shy
   B skillful   **D** strong

2 <u>industrious</u> worker

   A busy   **C** faithful
   B hard-working   **D** lazy

3 treated with <u>respect</u>

   A fear   **C** hatred
   B scorn   **D** honor

4 <u>boisterous</u> play

   A quiet   **C** loud
   B useless   **D** noisy

Read each set of sentences. Select the word or words that best complete the second sentence in each set. Fill in the circle for the answer at the bottom of the page.

5 We all went to the basement because of the <u>threatening</u> wind. <u>Threatening</u> means—

   A gentle
   B continuous
   C dangerous
   D blowing

6 The guards asked the <u>intruder</u> to leave. <u>Intruder</u> means a person who is—

   A a guest
   B unwanted
   C bad-mannered
   D a loser

7 Everyone should learn <u>self-defense</u>. <u>Self-defense</u> means—

   A love of oneself
   B pride in oneself
   C protection of oneself
   D respect for oneself

8 I have <u>confidence</u> that I will succeed. <u>Confidence</u> means—

   A respect
   B love
   C knowledge
   D strong belief

9 Every member of the family is a <u>conscientious</u> citizen. <u>Conscientious</u> means—

   A succeeding in all they do
   B becoming important leaders
   C trying to do the right things
   D threatening others

10 Perhaps you were too <u>aggressive</u> in your desire to win. <u>Aggressive</u> means—

   A willing to do any job
   B ready to start a fight
   C talented in every skill
   D too shy to play

11 Why do you study <u>martial arts</u>? <u>Martial arts</u> means—

   A a game played with a bat and ball
   B physical education
   C drawing and painting
   D system of self-defense

12 It was great to see the <u>respect</u> with which the players treated each other. <u>Respect</u> means—

   A high regard
   B roughness
   C friendship
   D helpfulness

ANSWERS

1	Ⓐ Ⓑ Ⓒ Ⓓ	4	Ⓐ Ⓑ Ⓒ Ⓓ	7	Ⓐ Ⓑ Ⓒ Ⓓ	10	Ⓐ Ⓑ Ⓒ Ⓓ
2	Ⓐ Ⓑ Ⓒ Ⓓ	5	Ⓐ Ⓑ Ⓒ Ⓓ	8	Ⓐ Ⓑ Ⓒ Ⓓ	11	Ⓐ Ⓑ Ⓒ Ⓓ
3	Ⓐ Ⓑ Ⓒ Ⓓ	6	Ⓐ Ⓑ Ⓒ Ⓓ	9	Ⓐ Ⓑ Ⓒ Ⓓ	12	Ⓐ Ⓑ Ⓒ Ⓓ

NOTHING FISHY ABOUT THIS WHALE TALE

The blue whale is the earth's most **enormous resident**. Sadly, though, whale hunters have killed and wasted too many whales. In 1978, all whales were declared endangered. It is now strictly forbidden to kill the blue whale.

The blue whale is four times larger than the biggest dinosaur. It weighs more than 20 elephants. Even though it **resembles** a fish, the blue whale is **actually** a mammal. Like all mammals, its babies are born. They are not hatched from an egg like fish. The blue whale has a few hairs on its head. It also has lungs. It needs **oxygen** to stay alive. The whale holds its breath underwater and will drown if it can't reach the surface to get fresh air.

A blue whale has no teeth, but it eats **constantly**. It has huge bony brushes in its mouth. As it swims, it swallows large **quantities** of water. The plants and animals flow in, and the brushes keep them from escaping. A blue whale can eat more than a **ton** of food a day. As you can guess, it takes a great number of tiny sea creatures to **satisfy** a "whale-sized" **appetite**.

FACT OR OPINION? YOU BE THE JUDGE

Are these sentences fact or opinion?

Write an F if the sentence is a fact or an O if it is an opinion.

1. _____ The blue whale is in danger of becoming extinct.

2. _____ The blue whale is the most interesting ocean animal.

3. _____ People should protect the blue whale.

4. _____ There are laws against killing the blue whale.

ALPHABET MAKES ORDER FOR WORDS

New Words

quantities	actually	constantly	satisfy	resident
appetite	enormous	oxygen	resembles	ton

Write the New Words in alphabetical order.

about

_____

_____   _____   _____

acute   enough   reserve

_____   _____   _____

                                                                    satin

                                                                    _____

                                                                    _____

WORDS AND MEANINGS MAKE SATISFYING MATCH

Use context clues or the glossary to match each New Word below with its meaning. Write the correct letter on each line.

____ 1. resembles	a.	a gas that has no odor and is needed by all living things
____ 2. constantly	b.	really; in fact
____ 3. oxygen	c.	a desire or wish for food
____ 4. enormous	d.	looks like
____ 5. appetite	e.	a measure of weight equal to 2,000 pounds
____ 6. quantities	f.	in a manner that goes on all the time; continuously
____ 7. resident	g.	much larger than usual; huge
____ 8. actually	h.	a person or animal who lives in a place, not just a visitor
____ 9. satisfy	i.	amounts or portions
____ 10. ton	j.	to meet the needs or wishes of

NEW WORDS FILL ENORMOUS SENTENCE HLES

Finish these sentences. Write a New Word on each line.

New Words

enormous

resembles

oxygen

constantly

ton

resident

actually

quantities

satisfy

appetite

1. The tomato is _____ a fruit even though it
   _____ a vegetable.

2. The elephant was _____ moving its
   _____ trunk from side to side.

3. It would take great _____ of pencils to weigh
   a _____ .

4. The blue whale is a _____ of the ocean, but it
   must come to the surface to fill its lungs with _____ .

5. Ben said that the only thing that would _____ his
   huge _____ was a juicy hamburger.

READER FINDS SYNONYMS ARE SIMILAR

Synonyms are words with nearly the same meaning.

begin and **start**
pick and **choose**

Draw a line to match the synonyms below.

1. enormous   a. really
2. resident   b. continuously
3. actually   c. dweller
4. resemblance   d. huge
5. constantly   e. likeness

11. fair   a. smart
12. intelligent   b. destroy
13. appetite   c. just
14. ruin   d. hunger
15. value   e. worth

6. quantity   a. desire
7. want   b. amount
8. steal   c. ache
9. flower   d. rob
10. pain   e. bloom

16. slender   a. grin
17. trade   b. vision
18. smile   c. thin
19. coarse   d. exchange
20. sight   e. rough

50

WORD SEARCH REVEALS NEW WORDS

Circle the New Words in the word search.

The words may appear vertically, horizontally, or diagonally.

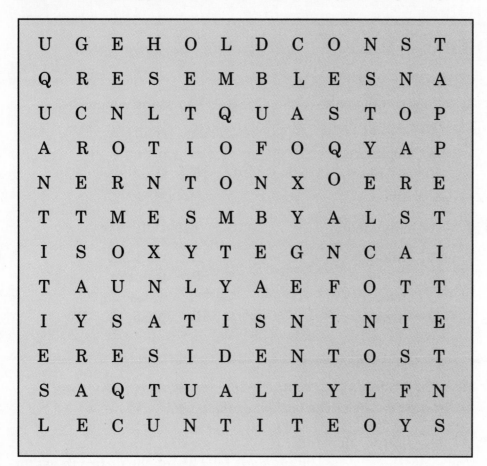

```
U  G  E  H  O  L  D  C  O  N  S  T
Q  R  E  S  E  M  B  L  E  S  N  A
U  C  N  L  T  Q  U  A  S  T  O  P
A  R  O  T  I  O  F  O  Q  Y  A  P
N  E  R  N  T  O  N  X  O  E  R  E
T  T  M  E  S  M  B  Y  A  L  S  T
I  S  O  X  Y  T  E  G  N  C  A  I
T  A  U  N  L  Y  A  E  F  O  T  T
I  Y  S  A  T  I  S  N  I  N  I  E
E  R  E  S  I  D  E  N  T  O  S  T
S  A  Q  T  U  A  L  L  Y  L  F  N
L  E  C  U  N  T  I  T  E  O  Y  S
```

REPORT REVEALS FACTS ABOUT ENDANGERED ANIMALS!

Write a research report on an endangered animal. Here is a list of some of them to help you get started. Check out the library for more information.

crocodile, alligator, manatee, rhinoceros,

Siberian tiger, whooping crane

These questions will help guide your writing:

• Why is the animal endangered?

• Why is this animal important to our environment?

• What has already been done to help this animal survive?

Use at least four New Words in your report.

A WHALE OF A TALE

• Schools of whales sometimes seem to commit mass suicide by swimming onto beaches. Even when they are freed and sent back out to sea, they will return again to certain death on the sand. No one can explain this strange behavior.

• The narwhal is sometimes called the unicorn of the sea. It has one long ivory tusk growing out of the middle of its forehead.

• The sounds that whales make are so hauntingly beautiful that they have been recorded and sold as music.

READ MORE ABOUT IT!

• *Why Are Whales Vanishing?* by Isaac Asimov. (Garreth Stevens Children's Books, 1992)

• *The Golden Book of Sharks & Whales* by Kathleen N. Daly. (Western, 1989)

• *Whales* by Gail Gibbons. (Holiday House, 1991)

Don't become endangered. Take the test!

51

IMPROVE YOUR SCORE

If you make a mistake, erase the wrong answer entirely. Don't forget to mark the correct answer for that question.

Complete each definition with the best word or words. Fill in the circle for the answer at the bottom of the page.

1 To be <u>enormous</u> is to be—

A small
B huge
C new
D old

2 A <u>resident</u> of a town is one who is a—

A guest
B leader
C dweller
D visitor

3 To <u>resemble</u> is to—

A watch
B look like
C fly like
D build

4 <u>Actually</u> means—

A really
B never
C usually
D always

5 <u>Constantly</u> means—

A really
B never
C usually
D always

6 To <u>satisfy</u> is to—

A work for
B talk to
C please
D push

Read each set of sentences. Select the word or words that complete the first sentence according to the stated meaning. Fill in the circle for the answer at the bottom of the page.

7 The divers will use tanks of _____ beneath the water. Which word indicates a gas that people and animals need for breathing?

A neon
B oxygen
C steam
D insecticides

8 We use small _____ of salt and butter at our house. Which word indicates amounts of these foods?

A quarters
B quotas
C qualities
D quantities

9 His small car weighs around one _____. Which word means two thousand pounds?

A tan
B ton
C tone
D tin

10 I lost my _____ for that kind of food. Which word tells about the desire to eat?

A appetite
B resident
C drive
D ambition

11 My dog _____ a little sheep. Which word tells that the dog looks like a sheep?

A is
B plays like
C resembles
D walks like

12 I am _____ being reminded to do my work first. Which word indicates that the reminders are very frequent?

A actually
B seldom
C constantly
D sometimes

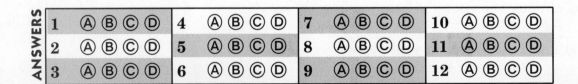

ANSWERS

1	Ⓐ Ⓑ Ⓒ Ⓓ	4	Ⓐ Ⓑ Ⓒ Ⓓ	7	Ⓐ Ⓑ Ⓒ Ⓓ	10	Ⓐ Ⓑ Ⓒ Ⓓ
2	Ⓐ Ⓑ Ⓒ Ⓓ	5	Ⓐ Ⓑ Ⓒ Ⓓ	8	Ⓐ Ⓑ Ⓒ Ⓓ	11	Ⓐ Ⓑ Ⓒ Ⓓ
3	Ⓐ Ⓑ Ⓒ Ⓓ	6	Ⓐ Ⓑ Ⓒ Ⓓ	9	Ⓐ Ⓑ Ⓒ Ⓓ	12	Ⓐ Ⓑ Ⓒ Ⓓ

NATIVE AMERICAN CODE HELPS WIN BATTLE

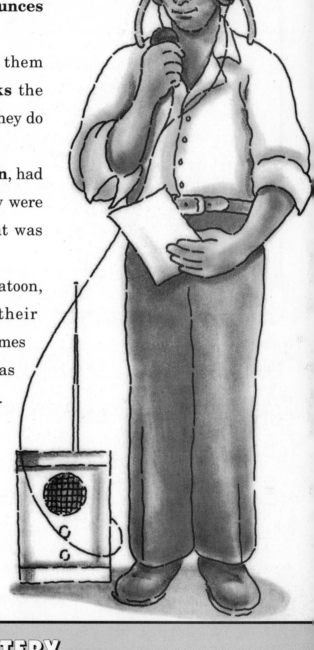

In 1941, bombs are dropped on Pearl Harbor, Hawaii. President Roosevelt **responds** quickly. He **announces** that the United States will enter World War II.

The Americans quickly develop a **code** that lets them communicate with each other. But the enemy **breaks** the code, causing the Americans to lose battles. What could they do about this?

Philip Johnston, who grew up on a Navaho **reservation**, had an idea. Since the codes were being broken because they were **translations** from English, why not create a code that was translated from the Navajo language?

The Marines decided to try his idea. The 382nd Platoon, which was made up of Navahos, **transformed** their language into code. They substituted Navajo animal names for letters in the English alphabet. When the code was complete, only the Navajo Marines could understand it. These men became known as the Code Talkers.

The Code Talkers were sent to Guadalcanal where they sent coded messages to the soldiers. The messages were **unbreakable**. In the battle of Iwo Jima, more than eight hundred messages were **transmitted** without **error.** Without the Code Talkers, the Marines couldn't have won this important battle.

SOLVE THE MAIN IDEA MYSTERY

What is the main idea of this story?

Check the best answer.

____ The United States joined the Allies in World War II.

____ Navaho Code Talkers broke the enemy's secret code.

____ Navajos developed an important secret code.

____ Many Navahos became U.S. Marines in World War II.

THE ALPHABET—A CODE FOR ORDER

Write the New Words in alphabetical order.

NEW WORDS

responds
transformed
code
error
translations
reservation
announces
unbreakable
transmitted
breaks

about

_____

attract

_____

_____

crimson

_____

_____

respect

_____

_____

_____

_____

transportation

_____

WORDS AND MEANINGS MAKE A MATCH

Use context clues to match each New Word with its meaning. Write the correct letter on each line.

____ 1. responds

____ 2. transformed

____ 3. code

____ 4. error

____ 5. translations

____ 6. reservation

____ 7. announces

____ 8. unbreakable

____ 9. transmitted

____ 10. breaks

a. answers; shows a reaction

b. sent or passed along, as a message

c. makes known publicly

d. impossible to solve or decipher; durable

e. a secret system of communication

f. written or spoken words changed from one language to another

g. solves; deciphers; causes to come apart

h. public land set aside for a particular use

i. changed; modified

j. mistake

NEW WORDS TRANSFORM INCOMPLETE SENTENCES

Use the New Words to finish these sentences.

1. It is interesting to observe how a pet _____ to its owner's voice.

2. I enjoy watching how a dog _____ that it wants to go for a walk.

3. Communication between pets and owners is almost like a secret _____ .

4. When a person _____ the code, a closer relationship between pet and owner develops.

5. My teacher spent last summer on a Navaho _____ .

6. She is making _____ of Native American folk tales.

7. One interesting tale tells how a member of the tribe was _____ into a piece of stone.

8. In the story, the hardness of the stone symbolizes the person's _____ spirit.

9. Yesterday I _____ a fax message to my friend.

10. An _____ occurred, and the message was not received.

WORD MEANINGS MULTIPLY

☞ Many words have more than one meaning. **Context clues** in a sentence can help you determine the meaning of a word.

For each sentence pair below, write the letter of the correct meaning on the lines. Look for context clues to help you.

____ 1. I asked our lawyer to write a <u>contract</u>.   a. become smaller

____ 2. A balloon will <u>contract</u> as you let out the air.   b. an agreement

____ 3. Jerry has a <u>wound</u> on his leg.   a. turned

____ 4. David <u>wound</u> his watch before he left.   b. injury

____ 5. Fred sings <u>bass</u> in our choir.   a. a low voice

____ 6. We caught six <u>bass</u> early this morning.   b. a fish

____ 7. Mrs. Carter gave the students a ten-minute <u>recess</u>.   a. set back

____ 8. My mom wants to <u>recess</u> the lights in the kitchen.   b. a break from work

BRAINSTORM BURSTING WITH IDEAS

Under each heading below, write down as many ideas as you can think of. Then go back and review your lists.

famous Native Americans

_____

_____

_____

famous military battles

_____

_____

_____

famous military leaders

_____

_____

_____

types of trophies

_____

_____

_____

professional football teams

_____

_____

_____

things that can be transmitted

_____

_____

_____

Decode the test! ── • ── •

GOOD THINKING

The Navahos kept the secret codes in their heads, so there was no code book to fall into enemy hands.

THE LONG SECRET

The Navaho code was never broken. It was top secret for twenty-seven years until the military developed newer methods to code messages.

READ ABOUT CODES

Navaho Code Talkers
by Nathan Aaseng.
(Walker, 1992)

SPY SECRETS REVEALED

 Imagine you are a spy on a secret mission. Write a paragraph describing how you would send a secret message back to headquarters. Then write a message using your own code, and translate it for your friends.

These questions will help guide your writing:

• What will your message say?
• What kind of code will you use?
• How will you get the message to headquarters?

Use at least four New Words in your paragraph.

SECRETS TO SUCCESS ON TESTS

If you have time at the end of a test, reread the directions and test questions.

Read each group of words. Select the word or words that mean the <u>same</u> as the underlined word. Fill in the circle for the answer at the bottom of the page.

1 <u>responds</u> to a request

   A refuses
   B ignores
   C replies
   D looks

2 <u>unbreakable</u> code

   A not clear
   B not able to be solved
   C not complete
   D never ending

3 written in <u>code</u>

   A Navaho language
   B English
   C secret language
   D numbers

4 <u>transmitted</u> messages

   A written
   B secret
   C sent
   D coded

5 <u>announces</u> a change

   A starts
   B creates
   C makes public
   D writes in code

6 <u>breaks</u> the code

   A solves
   B sends
   C writes
   D starts

Read each sentence. Select the answer that best completes the sentence. Fill in the circle for the answer at the bottom of the page.

7 Can you make ____ from your native language into English?

   A code
   B error
   C translations
   D unbreakable

8 Many Navahos still live on a ____ .

   A translations
   B error
   C code
   D reservation

9 The only ____ you made in this test was on the last question.

   A code
   B error
   C reservation
   D translations

10 Your hard work has ____ the basement into a beautiful recreation room.

   A transmitted
   B suggested
   C transformed
   D broken

11 He willingly ____ to all my questions.

   A announces
   B breaks
   C translations
   D responds

12 Have you ____ the message over the radio?

   A transmitted
   B made
   C reserved
   D transformed

ANSWERS

1 Ⓐ Ⓑ Ⓒ Ⓓ	4 Ⓐ Ⓑ Ⓒ Ⓓ	7 Ⓐ Ⓑ Ⓒ Ⓓ	10 Ⓐ Ⓑ Ⓒ Ⓓ
2 Ⓐ Ⓑ Ⓒ Ⓓ	5 Ⓐ Ⓑ Ⓒ Ⓓ	8 Ⓐ Ⓑ Ⓒ Ⓓ	11 Ⓐ Ⓑ Ⓒ Ⓓ
3 Ⓐ Ⓑ Ⓒ Ⓓ	6 Ⓐ Ⓑ Ⓒ Ⓓ	9 Ⓐ Ⓑ Ⓒ Ⓓ	12 Ⓐ Ⓑ Ⓒ Ⓓ

MARK YOUR CALENDAR FOR HUNDREDS OF HOLIDAYS!

What's your favorite **holiday**? Thanksgiving? Flag Day? Valentine's Day? Did you know that the **calendar** is filled with many special holidays, too? There is Be Kind to Mushrooms Day, Get a Different Name Day, and National Honesty Day. And May 8 is No Socks Day. The **sponsors** of this holiday hope that giving up socks will mean less laundry and a better environment.

We have these **unconventional** holidays because special groups ask for them. Congress sets aside special holidays, and each state has the **authority** to specify which holidays it will observe.

If you have older and younger **siblings**, then you can celebrate Middle Children's Day on August 13. Another special **observation** is World Hello Day on November 21. You can **promote** peace by saying hello to at least ten people.

Why not invent your own holiday to help get rid of some **frustrations**? Look around at your **surroundings** to get some ideas. Who knows, maybe your day will catch on and be celebrated around the world.

Humbug!

There is a movement on to form National Ladybug Day!

JUST THE FACTS, PLEASE

Are these sentences fact or opinion?

*Write an **F** if the sentence is a fact or an **O** if it is an opinion.*

____ 1.   Halloween is the best holiday.

____ 2.   May 8 is No Socks Day.

____ 3.   Saying hello to people will make the world more peaceful.

____ 4.   November 21 is World Hello Day.

ALPHABET PROMOTES NEW WORD ORDER

NEW WORDS

authority
calendar
unconventional
holiday
sponsors
observation
siblings
surroundings
frustrations
promote

Write the New Words in alphabetical order.

about

_____

_____

consonant

_____

_____

hunt

_____

_____

report

_____

_____

talent

_____

WORDS AND MEANINGS—A MATCH TO CELEBRATE

Use context clues to match each New Word with its meaning. Write the correct letter on each line.

____ 1. promote

____ 2. surroundings

____ 3. calendar

____ 4. unconventional

____ 5. authority

____ 6. holiday

____ 7. sponsors

____ 8. siblings

____ 9. observation

____ 10. frustrations

a. irritations; feelings of discouragement

b. a day set aside in honor of someone or something or to commemorate an event

c. the act of following a customary practice or rule

d. a chart of the days of the year

e. brothers and sisters

f. unusual; unique

g. persons or organizations that support or undertake responsibility for

h. decision-making power

i. environment

j. to help bring about

MISSING WORDS GO BACK TO WORK

Use the New Words to complete these sentences.

I look forward to every _____ throughout the year. I mark
each one on my _____ to make sure I don't forget. The holidays I like
the most are the _____ ones, like No Socks Day. Wouldn't it be great
to have the _____ to establish new holidays? I would find some
_____ to help me put new holidays into effect. One new holiday could
be Neighborhood Day, when people would celebrate their own _____ .
Another new holiday could be _____ Day, when people would do
something nice for their brothers and sisters. Celebrating a holiday can help some
people forget about their _____ . But _____ of
holidays is not something that appeals to everyone. Sometimes it's necessary to
_____ a holiday to make people aware of its importance.

SUFFIXES CAUSE NEW MEANING SENSATION

A **suffix** is a word part that can be added to the end of a root word to change the meaning
of the root word. The suffixes **tion** and **sion** can mean <u>act of</u>, <u>state of being</u>, or <u>a thing that is</u>.

For each word listed below, write the root word and the meaning on the lines.
The first one is done for you.

ROOT + SUFFIX	ROOT WORD	MEANING
a. creation	create	act of creating
b. construction	_____	_____
c. inspection	_____	_____
d. confusion	_____	_____
e. translation	_____	_____
f. completion	_____	_____
g. expression	_____	_____
h. reflection	_____	_____
i. action	_____	_____

UNSCRAMBLE THE MIXED-UP WORDS

Unscramble the New Words and write them on the lines.

NEW WORDS

authority

calendar

unconventional

holiday

sponsors

observation

siblings

surroundings

frustrations

promote

SCRAMBLED WORDS	NEW WORDS
1. rustitarfnos	_____
2. lidyaho	_____
3. sobretavino	_____
4. nelradca	_____
5. bilsnisg	_____
6. nocnevunnotila	_____
7. sopnosrs	_____
8. utahrotiy	_____
9. rorusunidgns	_____
10. ropteom	_____

EVERY DAY A HOLIDAY

 What new holiday would you like to create? Write a letter to a government official proposing a brand new holiday. Share your holiday with the class.

These questions will help guide your writing:

- What will your holiday celebrate?
- On what day of the year will your holiday be celebrated?
- Why should people celebrate it?

Use at least four New Words in your letter.

NATIONAL NOTHING DAY— JANUARY 16

A newspaper reporter created this holiday to give people one day when they can just sit without celebrating, observing, or honoring anything!

DID YOU KNOW?

➢ Approximately 900,000,000 Valentine's Day cards are purchased each year in the United States.

➢ More people make long-distance phone calls on Mother's Day than on any other holiday.

HAVE A HOLIDAY IN THESE PAGES READ:

- *A Book of Holidays Around the World* by Alice Van Straalen. (Dutton, 1986)
- *A Dictionary of Days* by Leslie Dunkling. (Facts on File Publications, 1988)
- *Ring Out, Wild Bells: Poems About Holidays and Seasons* selected by Lee Bennett Hopkins. (Harcourt Brace Jovanovich, 1992)
- "Oddball Holidays." (*Boys' Life*, December, 1993)

Celebrate the test! **61**

TEST YOUR BEST

If you skip a question in the test, be sure to skip that line in the answer box.

Read each group of words. Select the word or words that mean the __same__ as the underlined word. Fill in the circle for the answer at the bottom of the page.

1 <u>sponsors</u> of the holiday

- **A** opponents
- **B** supporters
- **C** agents
- **D** lawyers

2 handle <u>frustrations</u>

- **A** holidays
- **B** work
- **C** disappointments
- **D** games

3 enjoy the <u>holiday</u>

- **A** celebration
- **B** show
- **C** program
- **D** dance

4 <u>unconventional</u> practices

- **A** not correct
- **B** not usual
- **C** not easy
- **D** not forgotten

5 monthly <u>calendar</u>

- **A** meeting
- **B** chart of days
- **C** list of jobs
- **D** appointment

6 obeys <u>authority</u>

- **A** rights of an author
- **B** right to rule
- **C** parents
- **D** teachers

Read each set of sentences. Select the word or words that best complete the second sentence in each set. Fill in the circle for the answer at the bottom of the page.

7 The whole class worked to better its <u>surroundings</u>. Surroundings means—

- **A** grades
- **B** understandings
- **C** environment
- **D** circles

8 You can <u>promote</u> school spirit by taking part in the assembly. Promote means—

- **A** help something grow or develop
- **B** stand up and cheer
- **C** work against
- **D** start over

9 The <u>observation</u> of President's Day will be on Monday. Observation means—

- **A** date
- **B** holiday
- **C** celebration
- **D** day

10 Do you have more <u>siblings</u> than I? Siblings means—

- **A** cousins
- **B** grandparents
- **C** brothers and sisters
- **D** aunts and uncles

11 I can appreciate the <u>frustrations</u> you must feel. Frustrations means—

- **A** aches
- **B** pains
- **C** debts
- **D** discouragements

12 The government gets its <u>authority</u> from the people it governs. Authority means—

- **A** ability to spend money
- **B** power to make decisions
- **C** laws
- **D** flags

ANSWERS

1 Ⓐ Ⓑ Ⓒ Ⓓ	4 Ⓐ Ⓑ Ⓒ Ⓓ	7 Ⓐ Ⓑ Ⓒ Ⓓ	10 Ⓐ Ⓑ Ⓒ Ⓓ
2 Ⓐ Ⓑ Ⓒ Ⓓ	5 Ⓐ Ⓑ Ⓒ Ⓓ	8 Ⓐ Ⓑ Ⓒ Ⓓ	11 Ⓐ Ⓑ Ⓒ Ⓓ
3 Ⓐ Ⓑ Ⓒ Ⓓ	6 Ⓐ Ⓑ Ⓒ Ⓓ	9 Ⓐ Ⓑ Ⓒ Ⓓ	12 Ⓐ Ⓑ Ⓒ Ⓓ

AUSTRALIANS ROCK ON!

Rock-and-roll and Aboriginal music mix in the Australian band called Yothu Yindi. Yothu Yindi is composed of a group of musicians from a **remote coastal** town in Northern Australia.

Yothu Yindi's music comes from a variety of instruments. One instrument is a didgeridu (DIJ uh ree doo). A didgeridu is a long, hollow piece of wood that a player blows through. Didgeridu players **inhale** through their noses while they **exhale** through their mouths. Players change the shape of their mouths to make different sounds.

The town that the Aboriginal members of Yothu Yindi come from has only had **contact** with the Western world for about 60 years. This means that their **culture** has been unaffected by the West for over 40,000 years. Explaining their culture is an important goal of Yothu Yindi's music. Many of the group's songs are about **ancient** Aboriginal beliefs. Some songs **preach tolerance** among all people.

Manduwuy Yunupingu is the lead singer and songwriter. He hopes to bring Aboriginals and other Australians closer together through Yothu Yindi's music. Because of his efforts Manduwuy was **honored** as Australia's Man of the Year in 1992. He was the first Aboriginal to receive the award.

WHAT'S THE POINT?

What is the main idea of this story?

Check the best answer.

○ The lead singer and songwriter of Yothu Yindi was recently honored by the Australian government.

○ Yothu Yindi plays jazz music.

○ A didgeridu is a hollow wooden instrument.

○ Yothu Yindi blends music and cultures, using Aboriginal music and Western rock-and-roll.

THE AMAZING ALPHABET

Write the New Words in alphabetical order.

NEW WORDS

ancient
exhale
honored
culture
preach
tolerance
coastal
inhale
remote
contact

adorn

_____

_____

_____

continent

_____

_____

hermit

_____

_____

_____

remark

_____

_____

WORDS AND MEANINGS— A PERFECT MATCH

Use context clues to match each New Word with its meaning.
Write the correct letter on each line.

____ 1. tolerance

____ 2. remote

____ 3. preach

____ 4. inhale

____ 5. exhale

____ 6. honored

____ 7. coastal

____ 8. ancient

____ 9. contact

____ 10. culture

a. to breathe in

b. near or along the coast

c. at a distance; far-away; secluded

d. to give instructions or moral advice or to persuade

e. the beliefs, ideas, and customs of a group of people

f. revered or looked up to; given a token of respect

g. to breathe out

h. respect and recognition of other people's beliefs, customs, and actions

i. the state of being in touch or in communication with

j. existing in the past; old

MISSING WORDS FOUND!

Use the New Words to finish these sentences.

1. The distinguished physician took the microphone from the moderator to _____ about the dangers of smoking.

2. To _____ even secondhand smoke causes health problems for children and adults.

3. Archeologists recently discovered a village in a _____ and uncharted region of the Amazon Jungle.

4. They found _____ tools and artwork undisturbed by bandits who often raid such settlements.

5. With an increase in travel and trade, Europeans of the fifteenth century made _____ with people from around the world.

6. Europeans have _____ as heroes many of their adventurous travelers.

7. The doctor ordered the squirming child to inhale and _____ .

8. The boy needed immediate attention, so the doctor had little _____ for any interruption.

9. Kathy often sat on the rocks overlooking the sea in the small _____ town in New England.

10. The life and _____ of the town revolved around the fishing trade.

HOMONYMS—RHYME BUT NO REASON

☞ **Homonyms** are words that sound alike but have different meanings and spellings.

waste and **waist**　　　**flower** and **flour**

Choose the best word to finish each sentence.

1. I lose my _____ when I am on the telephone and am put on hold for a long period of time.   (patients, patience)

2. I went to the dock to watch the ship unload iron _____ into a freight car.   (oar, ore)

3. The young woman went to the _____ shop to pick a dress for her wedding.   (bridal, bridle)

4. What you told me just doesn't make any _____ .   (cents, sense)

5. I love to walk in the grass when it's covered with the early morning _____ .   (due, dew)

6. After the accident the man's _____ was noticeably different.   (gate, gait)

MEET THE ANALOGY CHALLENGE

☞ **Analogies** show the relationship between things.

reading is to **book** as **driving** is to **car**

big is to **major** as **small** is to **minor**

NEW WORDS

ancient
exhale
honored
culture
preach
tolerance
coastal
inhale
remote
contact

Use a New Word to finish each analogy.

1. _____ is to <u>hero</u> as <u>scorned</u> is to <u>coward</u>

2. <u>pyramids</u> are to _____ as <u>skyscrapers</u> are to <u>modern</u>

3. _____ is to <u>air</u> as <u>drink</u> is to <u>water</u>

4. <u>touch</u> is to <u>press</u> as _____ is to <u>blow</u>

5. _____ is to <u>far</u> as <u>close</u> is to <u>near</u>

6. <u>march</u> is to <u>walk</u> as _____ is to <u>talk</u>

MUSIC REVIEW

 Look at the picture. Write a paragraph describing what you see.

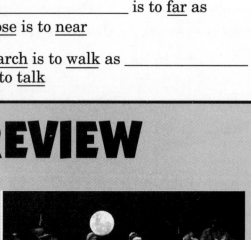

These questions will help guide your writing:

• Where do you think this scene is taking place?

• What type of music do you think the musicians are playing?

• What instruments are the musicians playing?

Use at least four New Words in your writing.

You are jammin' now. Take the test!

ROCK-AND-ROLL HISTORY

Did you know that there is a Rock-and-Roll Hall of Fame? It's in Cleveland, Ohio, where a disc jockey named Alan Freed supposedly coined the term "rock-and-roll."

COUNTRY OR CONTINENT? YOU DECIDE!

Australia is the only country that is also a continent. Although Australia is the size of the continental United States, it has only six states and one-fifteenth of the U.S. population!

READ ON, ROCK ON

• *Australian Aborigines* by Richard Nile. (Steck Vaughn, 1993)

• *Looking at Australia* by W.F. and R.A. Henderson. (Lippincott, 1977)

• *Live Aid* by Susan Clinton. (Children's Press, 1993)

• *Music* by Kay Rowley. (Crestwood House, 1992)

• *Concerts* by Kay Rowley. (Crestwood House, 1992)

TEST-TAKING SECRETS REVEALED

Answer all test questions of which you are sure. After you have gone through the test once, go back to the difficult questions.

Complete each definition with the best word. Fill in the circle for the answer at the bottom of the page.

1 To breathe in is to . . . .

  A exhale
  B inhale
  C preach
  D change

2 To urge or teach is to . . . .

  A inhale
  B preach
  C exhale
  D change

3 Something that is of times long past is . . . .

  A ancient
  B tolerance
  C culture
  D remote

4 To be treated with great respect is to be . . . .

  A remote
  B ancient
  C honored
  D composed

5 A willingness to allow other people to act and think differently is . . . .

  A remote
  B tolerance
  C ancient
  D culture

6 To breathe out is to . . . .

  A exhale
  B preach
  C inhale
  D change

Read each sentence. Select the answer that best completes the sentence. Fill in the circle for the answer at the bottom of the page.

7 The explorers made ____ with the Aboriginals when they visited their village.

  A contract
  B contact
  C contain
  D contempt

8 I want to learn more about the ____ of the Aboriginals to see how they live.

  A Rock and Roll
  B keyboards
  C tolerance
  D culture

9 Their village was so ____ that the Aboriginals weren't even aware of the Western World.

  A ancient
  B remote
  C coastal
  D honored

10 Peace will come among people when they learn ____ for each other.

  A culture
  B tolerance
  C beliefs
  D music

11 She was ____ for her achievements at a special dinner.

  A remote
  B electronic
  C composed
  D honored

12 The ____ area of a country is near the ocean.

  A honored
  B ancient
  C remote
  D coastal

ANSWERS							
1 Ⓐ Ⓑ Ⓒ Ⓓ	4 Ⓐ Ⓑ Ⓒ Ⓓ	7 Ⓐ Ⓑ Ⓒ Ⓓ	10 Ⓐ Ⓑ Ⓒ Ⓓ
2 Ⓐ Ⓑ Ⓒ Ⓓ	5 Ⓐ Ⓑ Ⓒ Ⓓ	8 Ⓐ Ⓑ Ⓒ Ⓓ	11 Ⓐ Ⓑ Ⓒ Ⓓ
3 Ⓐ Ⓑ Ⓒ Ⓓ	6 Ⓐ Ⓑ Ⓒ Ⓓ	9 Ⓐ Ⓑ Ⓒ Ⓓ	12 Ⓐ Ⓑ Ⓒ Ⓓ

BIOSPHERE II — LIFE IN A BUBBLE

Imagine being **confined** for two years within a huge **terrarium** about the size of three football fields. In 1991, eight people did exactly this when they were sealed within the glass walls of a **self-contained** world in the desert of Arizona called Biosphere II.

Biosphere II is a huge glass and steel **structure** that was designed to be a **replica** of Biosphere I, our Earth. Like Earth, it has an assortment of **habitats** including a desert, a marsh, and a rain forest. It has over 3,000 plants and animals and even an ocean!

Being a closed **ecosystem** where all living things within it work together to keep each other alive, "Bio II" is **airtight**. Volunteers who live there grow their own food, and their waste and water are **recycled**. The outside world provides only sun and electricity.

The experiment was not entirely without problems. After some time there was a shortage of oxygen, and volunteers spent **inordinate** hours growing, gathering, and preparing food. However, the crew set a record by living two years in a sealed environment. Perhaps the knowledge gained will one day help you live in a future biosphere in space!

CAN YOU DESCRIBE IT?

Which of the following does <u>not</u> describe Biosphere II?

Check the best answer.

____ glass enclosed

____ greenhouse

____ palace

____ terrarium

THE AMAZING ALPHABET

☞ In the dictionary, **guide words** at the top of the page mark the first and last entry on the page.

Write the New Words in alphabetical order between the guide words listed below.

NEW WORDS

confined

terrarium

self-contained

structure

replica

habitats

ecosystem

airtight

recycled

inordinate

action/emblem

_____

_____

_____

glide/jar

_____

rain/trumpet

_____

_____

_____

_____

_____

WORDS AND MEANINGS MAKE A MATCH

Use context clues to match each New Word with its meaning.
Write the correct letter on each line.

____ 1. confined

____ 2. terrarium

____ 3. structure

____ 4. self-contained

____ 5. replica

____ 6. habitats

____ 7. ecosystem

____ 8. airtight

____ 9. recycled

____ 10. inordinate

a. a likeness of

b. able to keep air from moving from one environment to the next

c. reused

d. natural environments

e. kept within certain boundaries

f. a frame or support; something built

g. the interrelationship between organisms and natural resources within a specific environment

h. an enclosure used to grow plants

i. containing everything needed within

j. extreme or excessive

MISSING WORD ALERT!

Use the New Words to finish these sentences.

1. The model that the students built was a _____ of the White House.

2. Its _____ was reinforced with metal tubing.

3. My grandfather built a _____ to grow tropical ferns.

4. He _____ scraps of food to use as compost for the soil.

5. The family was _____ in the basement for the duration of the war.

6. Although they prepared a _____ living space for themselves, they missed the company of their friends.

7. The desert of Arizona and the bayou of Louisiana are two of the many

   different _____ found in the United States.

8. We must protect our expansive _____ to protect the health of all.

9. The engineers unveiled an _____ vault for the storage of the papers.

10. Unfortunately, it took them an _____ amount of time to remember the lock's combination.

SUFFIXES MAKE BIG WORD CHANGES

☞ A **suffix** is a word part that can be added to the end of a root word. Adding a suffix changes the meaning of the word. The suffix **ize** means to make or become or act in a certain way.

Look at the meanings below. Add the suffix ize to each underlined word. You may need to change the spelling of some words.

MEANING	ROOT + SUFFIX
1. to make an <u>apology</u>	_____
2. to become <u>real</u>	_____
3. to make a <u>colony</u>	_____
4. to speak in a <u>general</u> way	_____
5. to act in a <u>formal</u> way	_____
6. to make <u>American</u>	_____
7. to make <u>popular</u>	_____
8. to become like <u>vapor</u>	_____

Need help?
Check out the
dictionary.

CROSSWORD PUZZLER

Use New Words to solve the crossword puzzle.

NEW WORDS

confined   replica   airtight

terrarium   habitats   recycled

structure   self-contained   inordinate

ecosystem

DOWN

1. vacuum-sealed or __
2. __ by a gate
3. A skeleton forms the __ of the human body.
6. complete by itself
7. Aluminum cans can be __.

ACROSS

4. to waste an __ amount of energy
5. regions with specific climates, resources, and living organisms
7. copy of an original
8. a habitat or environment where organisms and resources interrelate
9. an enclosed environment for plants

A BIOSPHERE STORY

Imagine that you could create your own biosphere. Draw a picture of what you think a biosphere should look like. Then write a story about it.

These questions will help guide your writing:

- Where is your biosphere?
- What do you think life would be like in a biosphere?
- If you could take only five items with you, what would they be?

Use at least four New Words in your story.

MORE ON BIOSPHERE II AND PRESERVING OUR PLANET EARTH

BOOKS:

- *50 Simple Things Kids Can Do to Save the Earth* by Earthworks Group. (Andrews and McMeel, 1990)
- *The Glass Ark: The Story of Biosphere II* by Linnea Gentry and Karen Liptak. (Viking Penguin, 1991)

 Recharge for the test!

SCORE HIGHER ON TESTS

Decide the meaning of underlined words before you look at the answer choices.

Read each set of sentences. Select the word or words that best complete the second sentence in each set. Fill in the circle for the answer at the bottom of the page.

1 Sam was <u>confined</u> to his room because of his injury. <u>Confined</u> means—

  A kept within   **C** given
  B kept out   **D** carried

2 A vacuum bottle is <u>airtight</u>.
<u>Airtight</u> means—

  A full of fresh air
  B full of stale air
  C open to the passage of air
  D closed to the passage of air

3 Biosphere II had its own <u>ecosystem</u>.
<u>Ecosystem</u> means a system of—

  A echoes
  B money
  C animals, plants, and bacteria
  D roots, seed, and bulbs

4 We <u>recycled</u> our newspapers.
<u>Recycled</u> means—

  A never used
  B used once
  C used again
  D seldom used

5 You are spending an <u>inordinate</u> amount of time on that job. <u>Inordinate</u> means—

  A too great   **C** just right
  B too little   **D** not enough

6 I don't think anyone can live in a completely <u>self-contained</u> environment.
<u>Self-contained</u> means—

  A self-centered
  B self-assured
  C self-sufficient
  D self-defense

7 Can you build a <u>replica</u> of this dog house?
<u>Replica</u> means—

  A a smaller copy
  B an exact copy
  C a dog house
  D a larger copy

8 The <u>habitats</u> of fish and seaweed are found in water. <u>Habitats</u> means—

  A lifestyles
  B places where they live
  C houses
  D families

Read each question. Select the word that best answers it. Fill in the circle for the answer at the bottom of the page.

9 Which word probably comes from the Italian word *replicare* meaning "to repeat"?

  A terrarium   **C** confined
  B recycled   **D** replica

10 Which word probably comes from the Latin word *terra* meaning "earth"?

  A habitats   **C** structure
  B terrarium   **D** biosphere

11 Which word probably comes from the Latin word *struere* meaning "to build"?

  A terrarium   **C** structure
  B self-contained   **D** replica

12 Which word probably comes from the Latin word *habitare* meaning "to dwell"?

  A replica   **C** habitats
  B structure   **D** inordinate

ANSWERS

1 ⒶⒷⒸⒹ	4 ⒶⒷⒸⒹ	7 ⒶⒷⒸⒹ	10 ⒶⒷⒸⒹ
2 ⒶⒷⒸⒹ	5 ⒶⒷⒸⒹ	8 ⒶⒷⒸⒹ	11 ⒶⒷⒸⒹ
3 ⒶⒷⒸⒹ	6 ⒶⒷⒸⒹ	9 ⒶⒷⒸⒹ	12 ⒶⒷⒸⒹ

SKATERS GET IN-LINE FOR FUN

you and your friends are talking as you bike along the trail in the park. Suddenly you hear the call behind you, "Passing on the right!"

Before you have a chance to think twice, several **figures** streak by, skates **whirring** and helmets **glinting** in the sun. You've just witnessed a new **trend** in sports—in-line skating.

In-line skating is the hottest form of **transportation** in town. It is something like ice-skating, but easier, because the wheels are wider than the blade of an ice skate. The more wheels you have on each skate, the faster you go. Beginners start with three wheels per skate, **intermediate** skaters have three or four, and racers have five.

Because the **equipment** is expensive, you may want to **rent** the skates at first to see if you enjoy the sport. If you do take up in-line skating, remember that a helmet, wrist guards, and knee and elbow pads are important. They help **absorb** the shock when you fall.

But skaters say the sport is well worth learning. Imagine gliding along almost effortlessly on thin wheels, **propelled** only by your strength.

GLIDING INTO THE MAIN IDEA

Which sentence tells the main idea of the story?

Check the best answer.

❑ Skating is the best sport of all time.

❑ In-line skating is better than biking.

❑ In-line skating is a fun new trend in sports.

❑ In-line skating is better than regular roller-skating.

SAVE ROOM FOR MORE WORDS

In the dictionary, **guide words** at the top of the page mark the first and last entry on the page.

Write the New Words in alphabetical order between the guide words listed below.

New Words
figures
whirring
glinting
trend
transportation
intermediate
equipment
rent
absorb
propelled

abacus/fight

_____

_____

practice/transmission

_____

_____

figment/intern

_____

_____

transport/whittle

_____

_____

WORDS AND MEANINGS MAKE CLOSE MATCH

Use context clues to match each New Word with its meaning. Write the correct letter on each line.

____ 1. figures

____ 2. whirring

____ 3. glinting

____ 4. trend

____ 5. transportation

____ 6. intermediate

____ 7. equipment

____ 8. rent

____ 9. absorb

____ 10. propelled

a. an up-and-coming idea; a fad

b. shining or reflecting light

c. being at a moderate level; in the middle

d. to take in

e. a means of traveling

f. to get temporary use of by paying a fee

g. forms; shapes; human bodies

h. pushed with great force

i. items or tools needed to accomplish a goal

j. making a steady, rhythmic noise

FILLING IN THE GAPS

Use the New Words to finish these sentences.

1. A bus can be an economical form of _____ .

2. Mass transit and alternative fuels may be the _____ of the future.

3. Paul passed his test and can now swim at an _____ level.

4. His upper body strength _____ him across the pool in the race.

5. I could hear the bicycle's tires _____ as the bicyclist tried to pass me during the race.

6. We would have to catch the two _____ in front of us for any chance to win.

7. It cost $15 to _____ the camping gear we needed to hike along the Appalachian Trail.

8. We did not want a lack of _____ to ruin our trip.

9. The _____ of the sun off the water on the road made it difficult to drive.

10. Luckily, it did not take long for the water to _____ into the road.

ANTONYMS—OPPOSITES ATTRACT

  Antonyms are words that have opposite meanings.

better and **worse**

take and **give**

Draw lines to connect each pair of antonyms below.

1. create	peaceful	9. fragile	expensive	17. freeze	horizontal
2. forceful	stale	10. guilty	innocent	18. vertical	melt
3. violent	part	11. cheap	shiny	19. failure	wise
4. whole	destroy	12. dull	tough	20. true	false
5. arrive	weak	13. tame	love	21. entrance	rude
6. fresh	leave	14. appear	straight	22. foolish	rich
7. capture	unusual	15. hate	wild	23. polite	success
8. ordinary	release	16. crooked	vanish	24. poor	exit

BE A SUPER SLEUTH!

Write the New Words that go with the clues below. Then use the number that represents each letter to discover the coded message.

1. autos, trains, and planes

<u>15</u> <u>18</u> <u>3</u> <u>12</u> <u>17</u> <u>19</u> <u>5</u> <u>18</u> <u>15</u> <u>3</u> <u>15</u> <u>6</u> <u>5</u> <u>12</u>

2. cleats, gloves, and helmet

<u>2</u> <u>11</u> <u>14</u> <u>6</u> <u>19</u> <u>28</u> <u>2</u> <u>12</u> <u>15</u>

3. popping, hissing, grinding

<u>4</u> <u>27</u> <u>6</u> <u>18</u> <u>18</u> <u>6</u> <u>12</u> <u>9</u>

4. shining, sparkling

<u>9</u> <u>8</u> <u>6</u> <u>12</u> <u>15</u> <u>6</u> <u>12</u> <u>9</u>

The Hidden Message

<u> </u> <u> </u> <u> </u> <u> </u> , <u> </u> <u> </u> <u> </u> ^K <u> </u> <u> </u> <u> </u> <u> </u> <u> </u>
<u>8</u> <u>2</u> <u>15</u> <u>17</u>   <u>9</u> <u>5</u>   <u>17</u>   <u>3</u> <u>15</u> <u>6</u> <u>12</u> <u>9</u>

<u> </u> <u> </u> <u> </u> <u> </u> <u> </u> <u> </u> <u> </u> <u> </u> ^K
<u>6</u> <u>12</u>   <u>15</u> <u>27</u> <u>2</u>   <u>19</u> <u>3</u> <u>18</u>

New Words
rent
figures
glinting
trend
intermediate
equipment
absorb
propelled
whirring
transportation

SKATING SCOOP

Look at the picture below. Imagine you are a reporter sent to watch a pairs figure skating tournament. Write an article about the event.

These questions will help guide your writing:

- Who was skating in the tournament?
- What type of skills are needed to be an accomplished figure skater?
- What made the winners stand out from the rest of the skaters?

Use at least four New Words in your article.

How fast can you take the test!

SOME READING AND WRITING TO GET YOU ROLLING

BOOKS:

- *A Complete Blader* by Joel Rappelfeld. (St. Martin's Press, 1992)
- *Get Rolling: A Beginner's Guide to In-Line Skating* by Elizabeth Miller. (Pix & Points, 1992)

ADVICE FOR BEGINNING SKATERS

▲ Avoid downhill slopes.

▲ Don't wear headphones that can keep you from hearing what's happening around you.

TEST-DAY TIPS TOLD

Get comfortable. You will be most comfortable over the length of the test if you sit back in the chair with your feet on the floor and your test paper directly in front of you.

Read each group of words. Select the answer that means the <u>same</u> as the underlined word. Fill in the circle for the answer at the bottom of the page.

1 form of <u>transportation</u>

   A buying what one needs
   B means of getting from one place to another
   C sailing
   D sending

2 pack the <u>equipment</u>

   A food
   B clothes
   C supplies
   D games

3 <u>propelled</u> into the air

   A sailed
   B flew
   C pushed gently
   D pushed forcefully

4 shadows of <u>figures</u>

   A numbers
   B forms
   C guesses
   D trees

5 the latest <u>trend</u>

   A wise advise
   B fad
   C news
   D gossip

6 the <u>whirring</u> motor

   A flying
   B buzzing
   C moving forward
   D moving quickly

7 <u>intermediate</u> level

   A middle
   B first
   C lowest
   D highest

8 <u>absorb</u> the water

   A give out
   B wash with
   C take in
   D pour on

Complete each definition with the best word or words. Fill in the circle for the answer at the bottom of the page.

9 To be <u>glinting</u> is to be—

   A gleaming   **C** staring
   B bubbling   **D** breaking

10 To <u>rent</u> is to—

   A buy from   **C** sell
   B pay to use   **D** borrow

11 To be <u>intermediate</u> is to be—

   A next   **C** before
   B between   **D** after

12 To <u>absorb</u> is to—

   A soak up   **C** think about
   B harden   **D** talk to

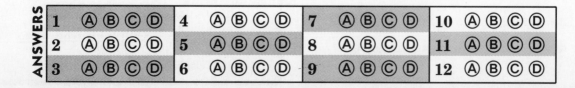

ANSWERS

1	Ⓐ Ⓑ Ⓒ Ⓓ	4	Ⓐ Ⓑ Ⓒ Ⓓ	7	Ⓐ Ⓑ Ⓒ Ⓓ	10	Ⓐ Ⓑ Ⓒ Ⓓ
2	Ⓐ Ⓑ Ⓒ Ⓓ	5	Ⓐ Ⓑ Ⓒ Ⓓ	8	Ⓐ Ⓑ Ⓒ Ⓓ	11	Ⓐ Ⓑ Ⓒ Ⓓ
3	Ⓐ Ⓑ Ⓒ Ⓓ	6	Ⓐ Ⓑ Ⓒ Ⓓ	9	Ⓐ Ⓑ Ⓒ Ⓓ	12	Ⓐ Ⓑ Ⓒ Ⓓ

AVALANCHE!

WHITE DEATH STRIKES WITHOUT WARNING

Avalanche! If you're like most people, that one word brings to mind an image of tons of snow roaring down a mountain. That's the **dramatic** kind of avalanche you see in the movies. Actually there are three kinds of avalanches. A dry snow avalanche **occurs** in extremely cold weather when the snow becomes dry and powdery. This loose snow **billows** down the mountain in swirling clouds.

Another kind of avalanche is the wet snow avalanche. It moves much slower than the dry snow avalanche because it carries wet, dense snow.

The third **variety** is more deadly. It is called the **slab** avalanche. It strikes more suddenly and is signaled only by a loud crackling sound. Seconds later, a huge chunk of snow breaks and falls, **demolishing** everything in its path. All kinds of avalanches occur when the pull of **gravity** becomes stronger than the **force** holding the snow on the mountain. This usually happens after a heavy snowfall.

An avalanche can travel at a speed of 200 miles per hour and crash like **concrete** when it reaches its final **destination**. "The white death," as the avalanche is called, strikes its target with deadly, earth-shaking violence.

CONCLUSIONS FORMED AFTER CAREFUL READING

What would happen if a town were in the path of a slab avalanche?
Check the best answer.

- ⭘ The avalanche would turn in another direction.
- ⭘ The avalanche would damage the town.
- ⭘ Buildings would stop the avalanche from advancing.
- ⭘ The people would leave the town before the avalanche hit.

GUIDE WORDS KEEP DICTIONARY ON TRACK

In the dictionary, **guide words** at the top of the page show the first and last entries on the page. All other entries on that page are in alphabetical order between those words.

Write the New Words in alphabetical order on the lines under the correct guide words.

billion/demerit

_____

_____

democrat/forbear

_____

_____

_____

forbid/occasion

_____

_____

occupy/various

_____

_____

NEW WORDS

demolishing	concrete	gravity
variety	dramatic	occurs
force	destination	billows
		slab

WORDS AND MEANINGS—
THE MATCH OF THE CENTURY!

Use context clues or the glossary to match each New Word below with its meaning. Write the correct letter on each line.

____ 1. occurs

____ 2. variety

____ 3. dramatic

____ 4. demolishing

____ 5. force

____ 6. concrete

____ 7. gravity

____ 8. destination

____ 9. billows

____ 10. slab

a. like a drama or play; interesting and exciting

b. happens; takes place

c. sweeps along and swells like a wave

d. any of the various forms of something

e. a flat, broad, and fairly thick piece of something

f. tearing down; smashing; destroying or ruining

g. the force that draws objects toward the center of the earth

h. the power to cause motion or to stop or change motion

i. a hard substance made of cement, sand, gravel, and water

j. the place that a person or thing is going to

NEW PARAGRAPH FINALLY COMPLETE

NEW WORDS

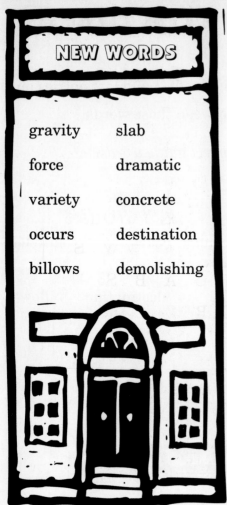

gravity   slab

force   dramatic

variety   concrete

occurs   destination

billows   demolishing

Finish these sentences. Write a New Word on each line.

We left at 4:30 in the morning. Our _____ was an old, empty building on Main Street. Since a new bank building was to be built on the site, they were _____ the building. The building had been used for a _____ of purposes, but we remembered it best as an old department store. The building was built on a thick _____ of cement. A special crew of workers had set explosives that would have enough _____ to knock out the bottom supports.

It was time. Even though most of the building was made of _____ , it fell to the ground in just a few minutes. _____ helped the building to collapse straight down upon itself. It was a _____ sight! In these photos we took, dust _____ from the area. An exciting event like this only _____ once in a while.

BREAK WORDS INTO SYL•LA•BLES

☞ Words can be divided into smaller word parts, or **syllables**. When you are writing a long word and come to the margin, the word should be divided between syllables and then continued on the next line.

Say each word and listen for the syllables. Write the words, leaving spaces between syllables.

1. variety   __va ri e ty__

2. dramatic   _____

3. destination   _____

4. demolish   _____

5. billow   _____

6. concrete   _____

7. gravity   _____

8. avalanche   _____

9. exclamation   _____

10. population   _____

Need help?
Check out the
dictionary.

READ MORE ABOUT IT

- *Historical Catastrophes: Snowstorms and Avalanches* by Walter R. Brown. (Addison-Wesley, 1976)
- *Avalanche* by Howard Facklam. (Crestwood House, 1991)
- *Avalanches and Landslides* by Jane Walker. (Gloucester Press, 1992)

WORD SEARCH MYSTERY NEEDS SOLUTION

Circle the New Words in the word search. The words may appear vertically, horizontally, or diagonally.

S	I	T	U	A	L	I	S	H	I	O	N
F	D	F	C	O	R	O	E	V	A	R	I
D	E	M	O	L	I	S	H	I	N	G	E
R	S	O	N	R	B	I	L	L	O	W	S
A	T	Y	C	S	L	G	A	B	S	L	
M	I	F	R	C	R	E	R	C	B	O	E
A	N	C	E	N	U	C	A	R	E	C	T
T	A	C	T	O	N	C	V	R	E	C	S
I	T	D	E	S	T	N	I	A	T	U	N
C	I	V	A	R	I	E	T	Y	O	R	S
D	O	R	A	M	A	T	Y	I	C	S	T
S	N	L	A	B	B	I	L	L	O	S	W

AVALANCHE SURVIVOR TELLS ALL

 Imagine that you are skiing and you see a small avalanche. Write a story with a friend about your dangerous adventure.

These questions will help guide your writing:
- Where were you when you saw the avalanche?
- What did you do?
- Did you get hurt?

Use at least four New Words in your story.

READERS BURIED IN AMAZING FACTS

- Snowflakes are crystals. Although they always have six rays, no two are ever exactly the same.

- It takes ten inches of snowfall to equal one inch of rainfall. That's because snow is full of cold air!

Slide
over
to the
test!

IMPROVE YOUR SCORE

It helps to have a quiet room in which to take a test. Do your part in keeping the room quiet.

Read each group of words. Select the word or words that mean the <u>same</u> as the underlined word. Fill in the circle for the answer at the bottom of the page.

1 a <u>dramatic</u> presentation

A exciting **C** musical
B boring **D** mystery

2 never <u>occurs</u>

A works **C** thinks
B happens **D** says

3 smoke <u>billows</u>

A sinks **C** forces
B occurs **D** swells

4 <u>variety</u> of shows

A stars **C** times
B kinds **D** names

5 a <u>slab</u> of rock

A flat piece **C** round piece
B mountain slope **D** thin piece

6 <u>demolishing</u> the truck

A building **C** driving
B smashing **D** buying

7 pull of <u>gravity</u>

A sun's rays **C** earth's pull
B machine's power **D** moon's weight

8 block of <u>concrete</u>

A cement **C** rock
B clay **D** sand

Read each question. Select a word that best answers it. Fill in the circle for the answer at the bottom of the page.

9 Which word probably comes from the Latin word *demoliri,* meaning *to pull down?*

A destination
B dramatic
C demolishing
D demonstrate

10 Which word probably comes from the Latin word *varietat,* meaning *various?*

A gravity
B variety
C destination
D slab

11 Which word probably comes from the Latin word *fortis,* meaning *strong?*

A gravity
B fame
C form
D force

12 Which word probably comes from the Latin word *destinare,* meaning *to fasten down?*

A demolishing
B destination
C dramatic
D defining

ANSWERS

1	Ⓐ Ⓑ Ⓒ Ⓓ	4	Ⓐ Ⓑ Ⓒ Ⓓ	7	Ⓐ Ⓑ Ⓒ Ⓓ	10	Ⓐ Ⓑ Ⓒ Ⓓ
2	Ⓐ Ⓑ Ⓒ Ⓓ	5	Ⓐ Ⓑ Ⓒ Ⓓ	8	Ⓐ Ⓑ Ⓒ Ⓓ	11	Ⓐ Ⓑ Ⓒ Ⓓ
3	Ⓐ Ⓑ Ⓒ Ⓓ	6	Ⓐ Ⓑ Ⓒ Ⓓ	9	Ⓐ Ⓑ Ⓒ Ⓓ	12	Ⓐ Ⓑ Ⓒ Ⓓ

"TERROR BIRD"
ONCE ROAMED NORTH AMERICA

If you had been a bird watcher sixty million years ago, you wouldn't have had any trouble spotting this feathered creature. No **binoculars** would have been **required**, either. What bird could this be? Its real name was diatryma, but its awesome appearance caused it to be **nicknamed** the "Terror Bird."

Diatryma rose to an imposing height of seven feet and was **incapable** of flying. The bird's short wings could not lift its **mammoth** body into the air. Instead, diatryma roamed the western **regions** of North America on its thick, strong legs. Each of its eight toes ended in a sharp claw. Its **stubby** neck supported a head with a huge beak.

There is some **confusion** among scientists over how the bird **obtained** its food. Some think it feasted on plants. It used its razor-beak to chop plants down the way farmers use tools to cut hay. Other scientists believe diatryma preyed on small animals. Everyone does agree on one **item**, though; diatryma was a giant. Its leg bone alone measured 23 inches long, and that is quite a big drumstick!

WHAT'S IN A NAME?

Check the best answer to complete the sentence.

Diatryma was probably nicknamed "Terror Bird" because it –

____ confused scientists.

____ lived so long ago.

____ had a sharp beak and claws.

____ had a frightening appearance.

EX PLORE THE DICTIONARY WITH GUIDE WORDS

☞ In the dictionary, **guide words** at the top of the page show the first and last entries on the page. All other entries on that page are in alphabetical order between those words.

Write the New Words in alphabetical order on the lines under the correct guide words.

NEW WORDS

binoculars

nicknamed

mammoth

stubby

obtained

required

incapable

regions

confusion

item

bingo/incalculable

_____

_____

incandescent/nice

_____

_____

_____

nickel/regard

_____

_____

regimen/stuck

_____

_____

_____

AVOID CONFUSION—MATCH WORDS WITH MEANINGS NOW

Use context clues or the glossary to match each New Word below with its meaning.

Write the correct letter on each line.

____ 1. regions   a. a pair of small telescopes fastened together for use with both eyes

____ 2. nicknamed   b. needed; ordered

____ 3. obtained   c. gave or was given a fun, affectionate, or shortened name

____ 4. item   d. not capable; not having the ability or power needed

____ 5. binoculars   e. very big; huge

____ 6. incapable   f. large stretches of land; areas or districts

____ 7. stubby   g. short and thick

____ 8. required   h. disorder or bewilderment; being confused

____ 9. mammoth   i. got possession of; acquired

____ 10. confusion   j. a separate thing; one of a group of things; unit

MISSING WORDS COME HOME TO ROOST

Finish these sentences. Write a New Word on each line.

Shawn found a huge footprint that must certainly have come from a

_____ animal. He imagined the animal to have a long body

supported by thick _____ legs. All day long Shawn used

his _____ to look for signs of the animal. The only

_____ he could find was the footprint.

Shawn spoke to others about his discovery. They had also seen footprints

but had been _____ of finding other evidence of the

creature's existence. The strange animal was reported to live in the nearby forest

_____ . It had been _____ "Houdini"

because it had escaped so many of their traps. There was much _____

about what kind of animal it was. No one had ever_____ a clear

picture of the creature. Shawn knew that a photograph would be

_____ before scientists would begin an investigation.

PREFIXES—A NEW BEGINNING

A **prefix** is a word part that can be added to the beginning of a root word. Adding
a prefix changes the meaning of the root word.

The prefix **uni** means <u>having one</u>.
The prefix **bi** means <u>having two</u>.
The prefix **tri** means <u>having three</u>.

Form new words by adding the prefix <u>uni</u>, <u>bi</u>, or <u>tri</u> to the words below.

PREFIX	ROOT WORD	NEW WORD
_____	cycle	_____
_____	form	_____
_____	monthly	_____
_____	cycle	_____
_____	annual	_____
_____	angle	_____
_____	cycle	_____

85

BIG BRAINSTORM HEADED THIS WAY

Read the following headings. What comes to your mind as you think about each heading? *Write down as many ideas as you can on the lines below.*

times of <u>confusion</u>

_____
_____
_____

<u>mammoth</u> things

_____
_____
_____

things observed with <u>binoculars</u>

_____
_____
_____

<u>items</u> needed in school

_____
_____
_____

<u>nicknames</u> of people

_____
_____
_____

things <u>required</u> for living

_____
_____
_____

RESEARCH THIS DINOSAUR DIVE BOMBER

 The pterodactyl was a flying reptile that lived in the age of dinosaurs. Write a short report about this extinct reptile. Use the encyclopedia or other reference books to find information.

These questions will help guide your writing:
- What did the pterodactyl look like?
- Where did it live?
- What was its diet?

Use at least four New Words in your report.

DYNAMITE DINOSAUR FACTS

- Some scientists believe that birds evolved from dinosaurs. According to this theory, birds' feathers developed from the lizard-like scales of their dinosaur predecessors.
- The diatryma was not the only strange bird of ancient times. The archaeopteryx was about the size of a chicken and had razor sharp teeth, a lizard tail, and three clawed toes on each foot. The hesperornis, with large paddle-like feet and no wings, spent much of its time under water.

READ MORE ABOUT IT

- *There Really Was a Dodo* by Esther S. Gordon. (H. Z. Walck, 1974)
- *The Passenger Pigeon* by Susan Dudley Morrison. (Crestwood House, 1989)
- *A Vanishing Thunder: Extinct and Threatened American Birds* by Adrien Stoutenburg. (Natural History Press, 1967)
- *Eyewitness Books: Dinosaur* by David Norman, Ph. D. and Angela Milner, Ph. D. (Dorling Kindersley Education, 1993)

 Roam on over to the test!

SECRETS TO SUCCESS ON TESTS

Go back to the story to see how the key word is used there. This will help you to see its meaning.

Read each sentence. Select the word that best completes each one. Fill in the circle for the answer at the bottom of the page.

1 I looked through _____ to watch the race.

   A regions
   B confusion
   C telescopes
   D binoculars

2 Shoes are _____ in the restaurant.

   A incapable
   B required
   C stubby
   D obtained

3 She _____ her car "Old Betsy."

   A obtained
   B required
   C told
   D nicknamed

4 He is _____ of understanding the seriousness of his actions.

   A stubby
   B afraid
   C incapable
   D ahead

5 I _____ this book at the public library.

   A required
   B nicknamed
   C bought
   D obtained

6 The circus was held in a _____ tent.

   A mammoth
   B required
   C obtained
   D stubby

Read each set of sentences. Select the word or words that best complete the second sentence in each set. Fill in the circle for the answer at the bottom of the page.

7 There are <u>regions</u> of Earth that are still not completely explored. <u>Regions</u> means—

   A animals   **C** buildings
   B areas   **D** cities

8 It is difficult to do this kind of work with <u>stubby</u> fingers. <u>Stubby</u> means—

   A short and fat   **C** long and thin
   B flat and wide   **D** long and fat

9 There is still <u>confusion</u> about who owns the car. <u>Confusion</u> means—

   A excitement   **C** anger
   B sadness   **D** disorder

10 I forgot one <u>item</u> at the grocery store. <u>Item</u> means—

   A group   **C** place
   B thing   **D** cart

11 The teacher <u>required</u> each student to write a report. <u>Required</u> means—

   A suggested   **C** insisted on
   B sold   **D** made a list of

12 The little child was <u>incapable</u> of seeing over the crowd. <u>Incapable</u> means—

   A afraid   **C** not able
   B against   **D** not afraid

ANSWERS

1	Ⓐ Ⓑ Ⓒ Ⓓ	4	Ⓐ Ⓑ Ⓒ Ⓓ	7	Ⓐ Ⓑ Ⓒ Ⓓ	10	Ⓐ Ⓑ Ⓒ Ⓓ
2	Ⓐ Ⓑ Ⓒ Ⓓ	5	Ⓐ Ⓑ Ⓒ Ⓓ	8	Ⓐ Ⓑ Ⓒ Ⓓ	11	Ⓐ Ⓑ Ⓒ Ⓓ
3	Ⓐ Ⓑ Ⓒ Ⓓ	6	Ⓐ Ⓑ Ⓒ Ⓓ	9	Ⓐ Ⓑ Ⓒ Ⓓ	12	Ⓐ Ⓑ Ⓒ Ⓓ

POISON PLANT PLOT EXPOSED
RASH REACTION EXPECTED

Does poison **ivy** have a **plot** against us? The plant looks pretty, but it can cause an itching, burning skin **rash**. The **source** of the trouble is the plant's sap. The sap contains an oil called urushiol. This oil is so powerful that a single **ounce** could **produce** a rash on 28 million people!

Avoiding the plant is not easy because it wears many **disguises**. Its green leaves usually grow three to a stalk, but they can be as small as a quarter or as big as the palm of your hand. In autumn the leaves turn yellow or red and blend with the fall foliage. People carelessly collect them.

Even poison ivy's name is misleading. It's not ivy, but a member of the cashew nut family. Cashews are harmless, but their shells contain urushiol.

In a **typical** case of poison ivy, urushiol slips through the skin in about five minutes. Nothing can remove it, and the itching begins. **Unfortunately**, more than a million Americans go through this itching each year. So let's **beware**! "Leaves of three, let them be!"

READERS ITCHING ABOUT INFERENCES
How are cashew nuts most likely sold?
Check the best answer.

○ in their shells ○ only to factories

○ already shelled ○ in plastic wrappers

GUIDE WORDS HELP KEEP ORDER

👉 In the dictionary, **guide words** at the top of the page show the first and last entries on the page. All other entries on that page are in alphabetical order between those words.

Write the New Words in alphabetical order on the lines under the correct guide words.

NEW WORDS

- typical
- unfortunately
- plot
- rash
- ivy
- ounce
- disguises
- produce
- beware
- source

beverage/itself

_____

_____

ivory/plight

_____

_____

plop/sound

_____

_____

_____

soup/unfounded

_____

_____

_____

_____

WORDS AND MEANINGS PRODUCE PERFECT MATCH

Use context clues or the glossary to match each New Word below with its meaning.
Write the correct letter on each line.

____ 1. ounce

____ 2. ivy

____ 3. unfortunately

____ 4. rash

____ 5. beware

____ 6. produce

____ 7. source

____ 8. typical

____ 9. disguises

____ 10. plot

a. a climbing vine with a woody stem and shiny leaves

b. a secret plan, usually to do something bad or unlawful

c. a breaking out of red spots on the skin

d. a thing or place from which something comes or is got

e. a unit of weight equal to 1/16 of a pound; a liquid measure equal to 1/16 of a pint

f. to cause; bring about

g. things that change the appearance or hide the identity of

h. being a true example of its kind

i. in an unlucky or unhappy manner

j. to be careful; be on one's guard against

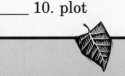

MISSING WORDS MAKE SENTENCES COMPLETE

Finish these sentences. Write a New Word on each line.

NEW WORDS

ivy

rash

ounce

disguises

unfortunately

plot

source

produce

typical

beware

1. Melting ice and snow from the mountain is the _____ of the river.

2. That actress often wears _____ in public.

3. The kilt is _____ of traditional Scottish dress.

4. _____ , Tammy had the flu, so we had to postpone her birthday party.

5. You should _____ of dogs that growl with their ears laid back!

6. Even a single _____ of gold is worth a lot of money.

7. One tree can _____ many bushels of apples.

8. Dr. Gordon said that the _____ on my arm would disappear soon.

9. The _____ has grown so thick that it covers the entire side of our house.

10. The police uncovered a _____ to kidnap a banker for a large ransom.

PREFIXES ADD NEW MEANING

👉 A **prefix** is a word part that can be added to the beginning of a root word.

Adding a prefix changes the meaning of the word.

The prefixes **un** and **non** can mean <u>not</u> or <u>the opposite of</u>.

Add <u>un</u> to the words below. Then draw a line to match each word with its meaning.

a. _____ fortunate   not afraid

b. _____ acceptable   not beaten

c. _____ afraid   not acceptable

d. _____ beaten   not fortunate

Add <u>non</u> to the words below. Then draw a line to match each word with its meaning.

e. _____ profit   not making a stop

f. _____ sense   not making sense

g. _____ resident   not making a profit

h. _____ stop   not a resident

ANALOGIES SHOW WORD RELATIONSHIPS

 Analogies show the relationship between things.

letters is to **words** as **numerals** is to **numbers**

letters : words :: numerals : numbers

Use New Words to complete these analogies.

1. _____ : skin :: rust : metal

2. _____ : create :: make : build

3. _____ : warning :: hello : greeting

4. inch : length ::_____ : weight

5. regular : irregular :: _____ : atypical

6. _____ : vine :: flower : bloom

READ MORE ABOUT IT

- *Poison Ivy, Poison Oak and Poison Sumac* by Donald M. Crooks. (U.S. Govt. Printing Office, 1978)
- *The Poison Ivy Case* by Joan M. Lexau. (Dial Press, 1983)
- *Watch Out, It's Poison Ivy!* by Peter R. Limburg. (J. Messner, 1973)
- *Crinkleroot's Guide to Walking in Wild Places* by Jim Arnosky. (Bradbury Press, 1990)

POWERFUL POISONOUS PLANTS

- There are over 700 species of poisonous plants in North America. Many are common in households and gardens. Here are a few that should not be eaten:

  azalea

  poinsettia

  iris

  holly

- Some poisonous plants are also the source of important medicines when prepared correctly.

PROTECT YOURSELF FROM EVIL IVY

 Learn more about poison ivy from an encyclopedia or other book. Then write a paragraph sharing what you've learned.

These questions will help guide your writing:

- Where would you most likely come into contact with poison ivy?
- Is touching the plant the only way you can get poisoned?
- What kinds of flowers and berries grow on poison ivy?

Use at least four New Words in your paragraph.

You're itching to take the test!

SECRETS TO SUCCESS ON TESTS

When more than one word could replace a blank in a sentence, be sure to choose the one that is asked for in the second sentence.

Read each set of sentences. Select the word that completes the first sentence according to the stated meaning. Fill in the circle for the answer at the bottom of the page.

1 We planted _____ to grow up the sides of the building. Which word indicates a climbing vine with shiny leaves?

   A fir   **C** spruce
   B ivy   **D** roses

2 The traitor was involved in a _____ against the government. Which word indicates the traitor had a secret plan?

   A fight   **C** rash
   B source   **D** plot

3 The poison ivy caused a _____ on my arms. Which word indicates a condition in which red spots appear on the skin?

   A source   **B** rash
   C plot   **D** rush

4 I took one _____ of the cough medicine. Which word indicates one-sixteenth of a pint?

   A pound   **C** ounce
   B gallon   **D** quart

5 The announcer told everyone to _____ of the coming of the storm. Which word indicates that the announcer was warning people to be careful?

   A beware   **C** plot
   B produce **D** feed

6 His _____ reaction is one of cheerfulness. Which word indicates that his reactions are usually cheerful?

   A rash   **C** typical
   B beware   **D** unusual

Complete each definition with the best word or words. Fill in the circle for the answer at the bottom of the page.

7 A <u>plot</u> is a—

   A product
   B secret place
   C rash
   D secret plan

8 To <u>produce</u> results is to—

   A plan for
   B bring about
   C plant
   D harvest

9 <u>Disguises</u> are things that—

   A plot
   B reveal
   C conceal
   D produce

10 <u>Source</u> means—

   A ounce
   B action
   C origin
   D plot

11 <u>Unfortunately</u> means—

   A anyway
   B sadly
   C truly
   D afterward

12 To <u>beware</u> is to be—

   A careful
   B fortunate
   C poison
   D warfare

ANSWERS

1	Ⓐ Ⓑ Ⓒ Ⓓ	4	Ⓐ Ⓑ Ⓒ Ⓓ	7	Ⓐ Ⓑ Ⓒ Ⓓ	10	Ⓐ Ⓑ Ⓒ Ⓓ
2	Ⓐ Ⓑ Ⓒ Ⓓ	5	Ⓐ Ⓑ Ⓒ Ⓓ	8	Ⓐ Ⓑ Ⓒ Ⓓ	11	Ⓐ Ⓑ Ⓒ Ⓓ
3	Ⓐ Ⓑ Ⓒ Ⓓ	6	Ⓐ Ⓑ Ⓒ Ⓓ	9	Ⓐ Ⓑ Ⓒ Ⓓ	12	Ⓐ Ⓑ Ⓒ Ⓓ

WOMAN TRADES TENNIS RACKET FOR SPACE RACKET

Sally Ride didn't know whether she wanted to be a scientist or a tennis player. In college she became interested in science, but she enjoyed and was good at tennis, too. After playing a doubles match with Sally, tennis star Billy Jean King told her to turn professional. When Sally "couldn't make the ball go where she wanted it to," she **abandoned** her tennis **ambition** forever. Instead she **focused** on science full time.

One day when she was in college, she read that the space program needed astronauts. She applied for the job and was hired! Five years later Sally became the first American woman to fly in space. Thousands of

"Rocket racket can't be beat!" astronaut declares.

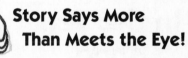

SPACE SHUTTLE ASTRONAUT HAS ROCKET SERVE!

people came to witness this **historical occasion**. Many wore T-shirts with the message, "Ride, Sally Ride." On the flight, Sally's most important **task** was to use a **mechanical** arm to **retrieve** a heavy **satellite**.

Since her flight in the space shuttle *Challenger* in June, 1983, Sally has become a role model for children everywhere. Had she taken Billy Jean's advice, however, Sally's **career** might have taken off in an entirely different direction.

Story Says More Than Meets the Eye!

Check the best answer.

This story suggests that –

○ Sally's decision to become an atronaut led to a successful career.

○ the space shuttle is a success because of Sally.

○ Sally was a better tennis player than Billy Jean King.

○ Sally made the wrong career choice.

GUIDE WORDS TELL THE SCORE

👉 In the dictionary, **guide words** at the top of each page show the first and last entries on that page. All the other entries on the page come in alphabetical order between the guide words.

Write the New Words in alphabetical order under the correct guide words.

abacus ■ foam	focal ■ observe
_____	_____
_____	_____
_____	_____

obtain ■ rock	rodeo ■ taste
_____	_____
_____	

New Words

retrieve

abandoned

ambition

focused

career

historical

occasion

mechanical

satellite

task

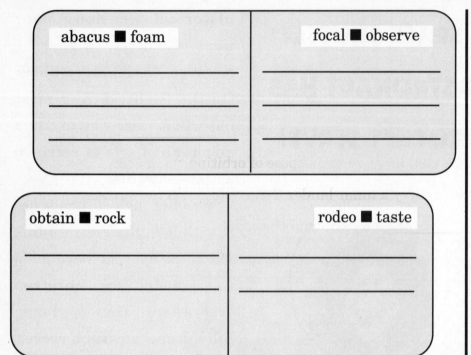

In the year 3000:

Did you know that the **historical task** of dogs was to **retrieve** bones?

No way!

Way!

94

WORDS AND MEANINGS MATCH

Match each New Word with its meaning. Write the letter on each line.

____ 1. historical   a. gave up completely

____ 2. abandoned   b. strong desire to be successful or to gain fame, power, or wealth

____ 3. mechanical   c. fixed or settled on some one thing

____ 4. career   d. based on what actually happened in history; not fictional

____ 5. retrieve   e. a special time or happening

____ 6. ambition   f. a piece of work that one must do

____ 7. occasion   g. made or run by machinery

____ 8. focused   h. to get back; recover

____ 9. satellite   i. an object put into orbit around the earth, moon, or some other heavenly body

____ 10. task   j. what a person does to earn a living

Sentences Take Off With Word Power

Finish these sentences. Write a New Word on each line.

1. The local _____ society bought the old Horace Burns mansion
on Oak Street.

2. It has been _____ for many years.

3. Their goal was to study Horace Burns' _____ and find out the history of the mansion.

4. The group worked with great _____ for several months.

5. They discovered a former president had visited there on a special _____.

6. This _____ was created for the sole purpose of orbiting the moon.

7. Its main _____ was to carry a lunar lander that could reach the surface.

8. After it landed, a camera _____ on unusual objects.

9. Then a _____ arm reached out and collected samples.

10. The arm was designed to _____ rocks as large as a small dog.

HOMONYMS
Serve Up Trouble for Careless Readers

☞ **Homonyms** are words that sound alike but have different meanings and spellings.

Write the homonym on the line that best completes each sentence.

1. Sally Ride is a good _____ model for children.
   (roll, role)

2. The _____ was blocked by stacks of boxes.
   (aisle, isle)

3. Jennifer has a _____ for writing poetry.
   (flair, flare)

4. I need to replace the right _____ on my bicycle.
   (peddle, pedal)

5. We learned about the life of a _____ when we studied the Middle Ages.
   (knight, night)

Need help? Use your dictionary.

Readers UNSCRAMBLE Word Mix-up

Unscramble the mixed up New Words.

Scrambled Word	New Word
1. casonioc	_____
2. ertereiv	_____
3. doedanban	_____
4. cosfued	_____
5. anchimelac	_____
6. ksta	_____
7. baitonim	_____
8. arcree	_____
9. sithailcor	_____
10. lastletie	_____

Racket / Rocket

DEBATE CONTINUES

Sally Ride had a choice of two careers, one as a tennis pro and the other as an astronaut. On another sheet of paper, write a paragraph telling which of these careers you would choose and why.

As you write, think about questions like these:

• What would your training be like for each career?

• Which career would be more rewarding to you?

• How might each career affect your personal life?

Use at least four New Words in your paragraph.

Blast off for the test!

TEST-TAKING SECRETS REVEALED

Look for clues in the sentence or phrase to help you understand the meaning of a word.

Read each set of sentences. Select the word or phrase that best completes the second sentence in each set. Fill in the circle for the answer at the bottom of the page.

1 The astronauts tried to bring the small <u>satellite</u> into the spacecraft.
<u>Satellite</u> means—

A radar station   **C** moon
B rock   **D** orbiting object

2 Each member of the crew had a <u>task</u> to do.
<u>Task</u> means—

A game   **C** job
B exercise   **D** question

3 The signing of the agreement was a <u>historical</u> event.
<u>Historical</u> means—

A imaginary   **C** happy
B important   **D** real

4 Sally Ride <u>abandoned</u> her desire to be a tennis pro.
<u>Abandoned</u> means—

A took apart   **C** completed
B gave up   **D** put together

5 The young doctor was happy she chose medicine for her <u>career</u>.
<u>Career</u> means—

A profession   **C** interest
B sport   **D** subject

6 An <u>ambition</u> of mine is to learn to water ski.
<u>Ambition</u> means—

A fear   **C** talent
B dare   **D** goal

7 The mechanical arm was used to <u>retrieve</u> the satellite.
To <u>retrieve</u> means—

A to steer   **C** to paint
B to bring back in   **D** to throw away

8 I welcome you to this important <u>occasion</u>.
<u>Occasion</u> means—

A party   **C** game
B homecoming   **D** event

Read each phrase. Select a word that means the <u>opposite</u> of the underlined word. Fill in the circle for the answer at the bottom of the page.

9 <u>abandoned</u> the project

A planned   **C** stopped
B gave up   **D** continued

10 <u>focused</u> her interest

A centered   **C** scattered
B stated   **D** expanded

11 a <u>mechanical</u> arm

A metal   **C** run by hand
B run by machine   **D** arm shaped

12 <u>retrieve</u> the satellite

A throw away   **C** inflate
B recover   **D** capture

ANSWERS

1	Ⓐ Ⓑ Ⓒ Ⓓ	4	Ⓐ Ⓑ Ⓒ Ⓓ	7	Ⓐ Ⓑ Ⓒ Ⓓ	10	Ⓐ Ⓑ Ⓒ Ⓓ
2	Ⓐ Ⓑ Ⓒ Ⓓ	5	Ⓐ Ⓑ Ⓒ Ⓓ	8	Ⓐ Ⓑ Ⓒ Ⓓ	11	Ⓐ Ⓑ Ⓒ Ⓓ
3	Ⓐ Ⓑ Ⓒ Ⓓ	6	Ⓐ Ⓑ Ⓒ Ⓓ	9	Ⓐ Ⓑ Ⓒ Ⓓ	12	Ⓐ Ⓑ Ⓒ Ⓓ

RUGGED BIKES PUT KIDS IN THE RACE

BMX is an exciting sport invented by kids for kids. The **initials** BMX stand for bicycle motocross. The X stands for the "cross" in motocross. BMX is **organized** bicycle racing over a dirt track with sharp turns and jumps.

The sport began in California about fifteen years ago. At that time, kids began riding their regular bikes on **rugged** trails. The kids got the idea from adults racing motorcycles. BMX bikes have no motors, though. They **operate** only on leg power. It was the kids who **adapted** their bikes to make them more **sturdy** for motocross. The bikes needed to be able to handle rough corners and high-flying jumps.

Today's motocross bikes have lower handlebars with a crossbar added for strength. They also have light frames and **knobby** tires. Another **feature** is the bike's specially **designed** wheel. A boy whose name was Alan Johnson suggested that a bicycle **dealer** build it. Can you guess what this wheel is called? It is the A.J., of course, in honor of the young inventor who gave his fellow BMX racers a much smoother ride.

NOTHING WILD ABOUT THIS GUESS

Check the best answer to complete the sentence.
From this story, you might guess that:

- ❏ BMX trails are in every town and city.
- ❏ BMX bikes cost less than other bikes.
- ❏ All children enjoy BMX racing.
- ❏ BMX riders need heavy-duty clothing to prevent injury.

GUIDE WORDS KEEP DICTIONARY ORGANIZED

👉 In the dictionary, **guide words** at the top of the page show the first and last entries on the page. All other entries on that page are in alphabetical order between those words.

Write the New Words in alphabetical order on the lines under the correct guide words.

adamant/feast	feather/knife	knit/rude	ruffle/style
_____	_____	_____	_____
_____	_____	_____	_____
_____		_____	

New Words

operate

designed

knobby

organized

rugged

dealer

adapted

initials

feature

sturdy

WORDS AND MEANINGS WERE MEANT TO MATCH

Use context clues or the glossary to match each New Word below with its meaning.

Write the correct letter on each line.

____ 1. adapted

____ 2. feature

____ 3. rugged

____ 4. dealer

____ 5. initials

____ 6. operate

____ 7. knobby

____ 8. organized

____ 9. sturdy

____ 10. designed

a. the first letters of a name

b. brought into being by working out the details; arranged in a particular way

c. having an uneven surface; rough

d. to control or manage

e. changed so as to make fit or usable

f. strong and hardy

g. lumpy or bumpy

h. a separate or special part or quality

i. thought up and planned

j. a person in business; one who buys and sells

> Need Help?
> Use the glossary on
> page 103.

MISSING WORDS DESIGNED TO FILL SENTENCE BLANKS

Finish these sentences. Write a New Word on each line.

New Words

initials

rugged

adapted

knobby

designed

organized

operate

sturdy

feature

dealer

1. The truck _____ sticks a decal with his _____ on the bumper of every truck he sells.

2. Larry _____ a group to search the _____ countryside for the lost children.

3. Ron _____ his jeep and _____ it so it would run in water three to four feet deep.

4. For his birthday, Scott wanted a _____ bicycle with _____ tires.

5. The major _____ of this best-selling car is how easy it is to _____ .

A L P H A B E T   S O U P

☞ Initials are often used to shorten long names of companies or organizations. If these initials form a word, they are called **acronyms**.

NOW stands for <u>National Organization of Women.</u>

Write the letter of the full name on the line next to each abbreviation or acronym below.

____ 1. NASA   a. World Health Organization

____ 2. HUD   b. Housing and Urban Development

____ 3. NATO   c. North Atlantic Treaty Organization

____ 4. POW   d. Self Contained Underwater Breathing Apparatus

____ 5. WHO   e. United Nations International Children's Emergency Fund

____ 6. UNICEF   f. National Aeronautics and Space Administration

____ 7. SCUBA   g. Radio Detecting and Ranging

____ 8. RADAR   h. Prisoner of War

THE GREAT PUZZLE RACE IS ON

Use New Words to finish the crossword puzzle.

ACROSS

1. drew plans
6. brought into being by work
8. changed to fit
9. strong
10. special part

DOWN

2. person who buys and sells
3. lumpy or bumpy
4. rough
5. first letters of a name
7. to control

EYEWITNESS ACCOUNT OF A BMX RACE

Look at the picture. Write a short paragraph describing what it must be like to ride in a BMX race.

These questions will help guide your writing:

• How do you get off to a good start?

• How difficult do you think it is to ride in a BMX race?

• How does it feel to take a high jump or a sharp turn?

Use at least four New Words in your paragraph.

Skid on over to the test!

DID YOU KNOW?

• At one time, bicycle racing was almost as popular as horse racing in the United States.

• The design modifications that make BMX bikes so sturdy are based on the design used in motorcycles.

READ ABOUT IT

• *BMX Racing: A Step-By-Step Guide* by Rod Alexander. (Troll Associates, 1990)

• *Learning How: BMX Racing* by Sue Boulais. (Bancroft Sage Publishing, 1992)

• *The Picture World of BMX* by R.J. Stephen. (Franklin Watts, 1989)

SCORE HIGHER ON TESTS

 Look over your test a last time to make sure you did not miss any questions and that your answers can be easily read by the teacher.

Read each group of words. Select a word that means the opposite of the underlined word. Fill in the circle for the answer at the bottom of the page.

1 organized games

   A board   **C** short
   B unarranged   **D** long

2 a rugged path

   A rough   **C** straight
   B winding   **D** smooth

3 a sturdy table

   A strong   **C** weak
   B wooden   **D** glass

4 knobby tires

   A smooth   **C** balloon
   B bumpy   **D** flat

Read each set of sentences. Select the word or words that best complete the second sentence in each set. Fill in the circle for the answer at the bottom of the page.

5 I signed my initials on the order form. Initials means—

   A first names
   B last names
   C first letters of names
   D nicknames

6 Baseball is his favorite organized sport. Organized means—

   A arranged in a specific way
   B played on a field
   C played with bats and balls
   D played by adults

7 The power stations operate on wind power. Operate means—

   A build   **C** produce
   B run   **D** make

8 I adapted the story for my little sister. Adapted means—

   A read   **C** told
   B wrote   **D** changed

9 The bright red color of the bike is its most outstanding feature. Feature means—

   A color
   B special part or quality
   C frame
   D ability to go fast

10 We talked to the bicycle dealer about the problems we had with the bike. Dealer means one who—

   A rides
   B buys and sells
   C builds and paints
   D races

11 A specially designed wheel makes the bike more sturdy. Designed means—

   A made   **C** turned
   B built   **D** planned

12 I did my work on a sturdy kitchen table. Sturdy means—

   A wobbly   **C** firm
   B clean   **D** painted

ANSWERS

1	Ⓐ Ⓑ Ⓒ Ⓓ	4	Ⓐ Ⓑ Ⓒ Ⓓ	7	Ⓐ Ⓑ Ⓒ Ⓓ	10	Ⓐ Ⓑ Ⓒ Ⓓ
2	Ⓐ Ⓑ Ⓒ Ⓓ	5	Ⓐ Ⓑ Ⓒ Ⓓ	8	Ⓐ Ⓑ Ⓒ Ⓓ	11	Ⓐ Ⓑ Ⓒ Ⓓ
3	Ⓐ Ⓑ Ⓒ Ⓓ	6	Ⓐ Ⓑ Ⓒ Ⓓ	9	Ⓐ Ⓑ Ⓒ Ⓓ	12	Ⓐ Ⓑ Ⓒ Ⓓ

GLOSSARY

A a

a•ban•doned (uh BAN duhnd) *v.* gave up completely

a•brupt•ly (uh BRUHPT lee) *adv.* suddenly; without warning

ab•sorb (ab SORB) *v.* to take in

ac•tu•al•ly (AK choo uhl ee) *adv.* really; in fact

a•dapt•ed (uh DAPT uhd) *v.* changed so as to make fit or usable

ag•gres•sive (uh GRES iv) *adj.* inclined to start quarrels or fight; actively bold

air•tight (ER teyet) *adj.* able to keep air from moving from one environment to the next

al•ter•a•tions (awl tur AY shuhnz) *n.* changes or modifications

am•bi•tion (am BISH uhn) *n.* strong desire to be successful or to gain fame, power, or wealth

an•cient (AYN chuhnt) *adj.* existing in the past; old

an•nounc•es (uh NOWN suhz) *v.* makes known publicly

an•noy (uh NOY) *v.* to irritate, bother, or make slightly angry

ap•pe•tite (AP uh teyet) *n.* a desire or wish for food

ap•pli•ca•tions (ap li KAY shuhnz) *n.* ways of being put to use

as•set (AS et) *n.* a trait or quality that gives advantage or profit

au•thor•i•ty (uh THOR uh tee) *n.* decision-making power

B b

be•ware (bee WER) *v.* to be careful; be on one's guard against

bil•lows (BIL ohz) *v.* sweeps along and swells like a wave

bin•oc•u•lars (beye NAHK yuh lurz) *n.* a pair of small telescopes fastened together for use with both eyes

blink•ing (BLINGK ing) *n.* rapid, automatic opening and shutting of the eye

bois•ter•ous (BOYS tur uhs) *adj.* loud; rude; ill-mannered

breaks (BRAYKS) *v.* solves; deciphers; causes to come apart

bron•co (BRAHNG koh) *n.* a wild or partly tamed horse

built (BILT) *v.* constructed; made

bur•ro (BUR oh) *n.* a small donkey

C c

cal•en•dar (KAL uhn dur) *n.* a chart of the days of the year

ca•reer (kuh RIR) *n.* what a person does to earn a living

cav•i•ty (KAV i tee) *n.* a hole or open area

child•hood (CHEYELD hud) *n.* the condition or time of being young, not adult

click•ing (KLIK ing) *adj.* making or causing a light tapping

coast•al (KOHS tuhl) *adj.* near or along the coast

code (KOHD) *n.* a secret system of communication

com•pet•i•tive (kuhm PET i tiv) *adj.* related to competition; driven to compete

con•crete (KAHN kreet) *n.* a hard substance made of cement, sand, gravel, and water

con•fi•dence (KAHN fi duhns) *n.* belief in one's own powers and abilities

con•fined (kuhn FEYEND) *v.* kept within certain boundaries

con•fu•sion (kuhn FYOO zhuhn) *n.* disorder or bewilderment; being confused

con•sci•en•tious (kahn shee EN shuhs) *adj.* careful; showing great attention to detail; honest

con•stant•ly (KAHN stuhnt lee) *adv.* in a manner that goes on all the time; continuously

con•sum•er (kuhn SOO mur) *n.* one who buys and uses

con•tact (KAHN takt) *n.* the state of being in touch or in communication with

con•trac•tions (kuhn TRAK shuhnz) *n.* the shortening or pulling inward of muscles

con•ver•sa•tion (kahn vur SAY shuhn) *n.* talk between two or more people

co•or•di•na•tion (koh or di NAY shuhn) *n.* the ability to act together in a smooth way

cul•ture (KUL chur) *n.* the beliefs, ideas, and customs of a group of people

D d

deal•er (DEEL ur) *n.* a person in business; one who buys and sells

de•mol•ish•ing (dee MAHL ish ing) *v.* tearing down; smashing; destroying or ruining

de•signed (dee ZEYEND) *adj.* thought up and planned

des•ti•na•tion (des ti NAY shuhn) *n.* the place that a person or thing is going to

di•a•phragm (DEYE uh fram) *n.* a large muscle at the base of the chest area, used for breathing

dis•guis•es (dis GEYEZ uhz) *n.* things that change the appearance or hide the identity of

dis•tin•guished (di STING gwishd) *adj.* known for being excellent; celebrated

dra•mat•ic (druh MAT ik) *adj.* like a drama or play; interesting and exciting

E e

ech•oes (EK oz) *n.* sounds heard when sound waves bounce back from a surface

ec•o•sys•tem (EE koh sis tuhm) *n.* the interrelationship between organisms and natural resources within a specific environment

ed•u•ca•tion (ej oo KAY shuhn) *n.* the process of developing knowledge or skill

en•cased (en KAYST) *v.* enclosed or surrounded

en•dur•ance (en DYUR uhns) *n.* strength; ability to last

e•nor•mous (ee NOR muhs) *adj.* much larger than usual; huge

en•vi•ron•ment (en VEYE ruhn muhnt) *n.* all the conditions that surround a person, animal, or plant and affect such things as growth and actions

e•quip•ment (ee KWIP muhnt) *n.* items or tools needed to accomplish a goal

er•ror (ER ur) *n.* mistake

es•tab•lished (e STAB lisht) *v.* caused to be; set up

ex•hale (eks HAYL) *v.* to breathe out

F f

fa•mil•iar (fuh MIL yur) *adj.* well-known; recognizable

fea•ture (FEE chur) *n.* a separate or special part or quality

fig•ures (FIG yurz) *n.* forms; shapes; human bodies

flu•id (FLOO id) *n.* a flowing liquid or gas

fo•cused (FOH kuhst) *v.* fixed or settled on some one thing

folk•lore (FOHK lor) *n.* traditional customs, sayings, and stories of a people

force (FORS) *n.* the power to cause motion or to stop or change motion

frus•tra•tions (fruhs TRAY shuhnz) *n.* irritations; feelings of discouragement

G g

germs (JURMZ) *n.* microscopic organisms that cause disease

glands (GLANDZ) *n.* body organs that produce and secrete bodily fluids

glint•ing (GLINT ing) *v.* shining or reflecting light

grad•u•at•ed (GRA joo ay tuhd) *v.* received an academic degree or diploma

grav•i•ty (GRAV i tee) *n.* the force that draws objects toward the center of the earth

gym•na•si•um (jim NAY zee uhm) *n.* a place for physical exercise

H h

hab•i•tats (HAB i tats) *n.* natural environments

height (HEYET) *n.* a relatively great distance from bottom to top

hic•cup (HIK uhp) *v.* to inhale abruptly from an involuntary contraction of the diaphragm, producing a sharp sound

his•tor•i•cal (his TOR i kuhl) *adj.* based on what actually happened in history; not fictional

hol•i•day (HAHL i day) *n.* a day set aside in honor of someone or something or to commemorate an event

hon•ored (AHN urd) *v.* revered or looked up to; given a token of respect

I i

im•age (IM ij) *n.* a general impression of what a person or thing is

in•ca•pa•ble (in KAY puh buhl) *adj.* not capable; not having the ability or power needed

in•dus•tri•ous (in DUS tree uhs) *adj.* hard-working; busy

in•hale (in HAYL) *v.* to breathe in

in•i•tials (i NISH uhlz) *n.* the first letters of a name

in•or•di•nate (in OR duh nit) *adj.* extreme or excessive

in•sec•ti•cides (in SEK ti seyedz) *n.* poisons used to kill insects

in•spires (in SPEYERZ) *v.* influences or motivates by example

in•ter•me•di•ate (in tur MEE dee uht) *adj.* being at a moderate level; in the middle

in•tim•i•date (in TIM uh dayt) *v.* to dominate or frighten

in•trud•er (in TROOD ur) *n.* unwanted visitor

ir•ri•tate (IR uh tayt) *v.* to make something sore or sensitive

i•tem (EYET uhm) *n.* a separate thing; one of a group of things; unit

i•vy (EYE vee) *n.* climbing vine with a woody stem and shiny leaves

J J

jour•nal•ism (JUR nuhl iz uhm) *n.* the collection and presentation of news

K k

knob•by (NAHB ee) *adj.* lumpy or bumpy

L l

lit•er•a•ture (LIT ur uh chur) *n.* writing of great and lasting value

M m

mam•mals (MAM uhlz) *n.* warm-blooded animals with glands in the female that produce milk for feeding its young

mam•moth (MAM uhth) *adj.* very big; huge

ma•neu•ver (muh NOO vur) *v.* to make a series of changes in direction or position

mar•tial arts (MAHR shuhl AHRTS) *n.* the various systems of self-defense

me•chan•i•cal (mi KAN i kuhl) *adj.* made or run by machinery

mu•cus (MYOO kuhs) *n.* a thick secretion of the body that moistens and protects

N n

nick•named (NIK naymd) *v.* gave or was given a fun, affectionate, or shortened name

No•bel Prize (noh BEL PREYEZ) *n.* a prize given once a year for excellence in the sciences or literature or for promoting peace

ob·ser·va·tion (ahb zur VAY shuhn) *n.* the act of following a customary practice or rule

ob·tained (ahb TAYND) *v.* got possession of; acquired

oc·ca·sion (oh KAY zhuhn) *n.* a special time or happening

oc·curs (uh KURZ) *v.* happens; takes place

op·er·ate (AHP ur ayt) *v.* to control or manage

or·gan·ized (OR guh neyezd) *adj.* brought into being by working out the details; arranged in a particular way

ounce (OWNS) *n.* a unit of weight equal to 1/16 of a pound; a liquid measure equal to 1/16 of a pint

o·ver·hand (OH vur hand) *adv.* with the hand or hands above the head

ox·y·gen (AHKS i juhn) *n.* a gas that has no odor and is needed by all living things

P p

par·tic·i·pate (pahr TIS i payt) *v.* take part in

pa·ti·o (PAT ee oh) *n.* a paved area next to a house for outdoor dining or lounging

pests (PESTS) *n.* persons or things that cause trouble, especially insects or small animals that destroy things

phys·i·cal (FIZ i kuhl) *adj.* having to do with the body

pla·za (PLAZ uh) *n.* a public square or courtyard

plot (PLAHT) *n.* a secret plan, usually to do something bad or unlawful

pol·lu·tants (puh LOOT nts) *n.* things that add dirt or impurities

pop·u·la·tions (pahp yoo LAY shuhnz) *n.* groups of people or animals living in a certain area or place

po·ten·tial (poh TEN shuhl) *n.* a quality capable of being developed; possibility

preach (PREECH) *v.* to give instructions or moral advice or to persuade

pro·duce (proh DOOS) *v.* to cause; bring about

pro·mote (proh MOHT) *v.* to help bring about

pron·to (PRAHN toh) *adv.* right away; without delay

pro·pelled (proh PELD) *v.* pushed with great force

pub·lish·ing (PUHB lish ing) *adj.* making and selling books

pu·ri·fi·ers (PYUR uh feye urz) *n.* things that eliminate dirt or impurities

Q q

quan·ti·ties (KWAHN ti teez) *n.* amounts or portions

R r

rash (RASH) *n.* a breaking out of red spots on the skin

rec·re·a·tion (rek ree AY shuhn) *n.* enjoyable pastime; any form of amusement or relaxation

re·cy·cled (ree SEYE kuhld) *v.* reused

re·fur·bished (ree FUR bisht) *adj.* renovated; freshened up

re·gions (REE juhnz) *n.* large stretches of land; areas or districts

rem·e·dies (REM uh deez) *n.* cures or solutions

re·mote (ree MOHT) *adj.* at a distance; faraway; secluded

rent (RENT) *v.* to get temporary use of by paying a fee

rep·li·ca (REP li kuh) *n.* a likeness of

re·quired (ree KWEYERD) *v.* needed; ordered

re·sem·bles (ree ZEM buhlz) *v.* looks like

res·er·va·tion (rez ur VAY shuhn) *n.* public land set aside for a particular use

res·i·dent (REZ i duhnt) *n.* a person or animal who lives in a place, not just a visitor

re·spect (ree SPEKT) *n.* high regard; esteem

re·sponds (ree SPAHNDZ) *v.* answers; shows a reaction

re·trieve (ri TREEV) *v.* to get back; recover

rhyth·mic (RITH mik) *adj.* occurring at regular intervals

ro·de·o (ROH dee oh) *n.* a cowboy show

rug·ged (RUHG uhd) *adj.* having an uneven surface; rough

S s

sat·el·lite (SAT l eyet) *n.* an object put into orbit around the earth, moon, or some other heavenly body

sat·is·fy (SAT is feye) *v.* to meet the needs or wishes of

sa·vor (SAY vur) *v.* to enjoy a pleasing sensation

se·crete (suh KREET) *v.* to form and give off

se·cu·ri·ty (si KYUR i tee) *adj.* safety from harm

self-con•tained (SELF kuhn TAYND) *adj.*
containing everything needed within

self-de•fense (SELF dee FENS) *n.* protection
of oneself

served (SURVD) *v.* put a ball into play during
a game

sib•lings (SIB lingz) *n.* brothers and sisters

skull (SKUHL) *n.* the bones of the head

slab (SLAB) *n.* a flat, broad, and fairly thick
piece of something

source (SORS) *n.* a thing or place from which
something comes or is got

spasm (SPAZ uhm) *n.* a sudden, involuntary
muscle tightening

spe•cies (SPEE sheez) *n.* a group of plants or
animals that are alike in certain ways

spi•nal cord (SPEYE nuhl KORD) *n.* a thick
bundle of nerves running through the
backbone

spon•sors (SPAHN surz) *n.* persons or
organizations that support or undertake
responsibility for

struc•ture (STRUHK chur) *n.* a frame or
support; something built

stub•by (STUB ee) *adj.* short and thick

stur•dy (STUR dee) *adj.* strong and hardy

sur•round•ings (sur ROWN dingz) *n.*
environment

sus•pen•sions (suh SPEN shuhnz) *n.*
supporting frameworks

T t

ta•cos (TAH kohz) *n.* folded tortillas with some
sort of filling, usually beef or beans

task (TASK) *n.* a piece of work that one must
do

tear (TIR) *n.* a clear, salty fluid secreted by
glands in the eyes

tech•nol•o•gy (tek NAHL uh jee) *n.* the use of
scientific discoveries for practical purposes

ter•rain (tuh RAYN) *n.* a piece of land with
particular features

ter•rar•i•um (tuh RER ee uhm) n. an enclosure
used to grow plants

threat•en•ing (THRET n ing) *adj.* giving signs
of an intent to do harm

tol•er•ance (TAHL ur uhns) *n.* respect and
recognition of other people's beliefs, customs,
and actions

ton (TUHN) *n.* a measure of weight equal to
2,000 pounds

tor•til•las (tor TEE uhz) *n.* flat cakes or breads
made of cornmeal

trans•formed (trans FORMD) *v.* changed;
modified

trans•la•tions (trans LAY shuhnz) *n.* written or
spoken words changed from one language to
another

trans•mit•ted (trans MIT uhd) *v.* sent or passed
along, as a message

trans•por•ta•tion (trans pur TAY shuhn) *n.* a
means of traveling

trend (TREND) *n.* an up-and-coming idea; a fad

typ•i•cal (TIP i kuhl) *adj.* being a true example
of its kind

U u

un•break•a•ble (uhn BRAYK uh buhl) *adj.*
impossible to solve or decipher; durable

un•con•ven•tion•al (uhn kuhn VEN shuh nuhl)
adj. unusual; unique

un•for•tu•nate•ly (uhn FOR chuh nuht lee) *adv.*
in an unlucky or unhappy manner

V v

va•nil•la (vuh NIL uh) *n.* a flavoring used in
cooking

va•ri•e•ty (vuh REYE uh tee) *n.* any of the
various forms of something

ver•ti•cal (VUR ti kuhl) *adj.* perpendicular to
the horizon

vid•e•o (VID ee oh) *adj.* relating to the sending
or receiving of images on a television or other
electronic screen

vol•ley•ball (VAHL ee bawl) *n.* a game in which
two teams hit a ball across a high net; a type of
ball

W w

whir•ring (HWUR ing) *v.* making a steady,
rhythmic noise

Answer Key

Volleyball Serves Up Fun
pages 3-7

Main Idea Sets Up Story
the game of volleyball

Alphabet at Your Service
1. asset
2. education
3. gymnasium
4. height
5. overhand
6. participate
7. physical
8. served
9. vertical
10. volleyball

Words and Meanings Make Exciting Match
1. a
2. c
3. e
4. g
5. h
6. f
7. i
8. d
9. j
10. b

New Words Finish Sentences
1. vertical
2. education
3. gymnasium
4. volleyball
5. height
6. physical
7. overhand
8. participate
9. served
10. asset

Suffixes at Work
a. denial, act of denying
b. arrival, act of arriving
c. musical, of music
d. magical, like magic
e. refusal, act of refusing
f. dismissal, act of dismissing

Analogies Make Meaningful Relationships
1. overhand
2. physical
3. height
4. asset
5. vertical
6. participate

Test-taking Secrets Revealed
1. A
2. D
3. D
4. C
5. B
6. B
7. B
8. D
9. D
10. C
11. B
12. B

Can You Speak Spanish?
pages 8-12

Si (Yes) or No?
1. Si
2. Si
3. No
4. No

Alphabet Works in Many Languages
1. bronco
2. burro
3. conversation
4. patio
5. plaza
6. pronto
7. rodeo
8. tacos
9. tortillas
10. vanilla

Words and Meanings Match
1. a
2. c
3. e
4. g
5. i
6. b
7. h
8. f
9. j
10. d

New Words Fill Sentence Holes
1. rodeo
2. bronco
3. tortillas
4. tacos
5. conversation
6. plaza
7. patio
8. pronto
9. burro
10. vanilla

Don't Be Fooled by Homonyms
1. d
2. e
3. a
4. c
5. b
6. c
7. e
8. a
9. b
10. d

a. peak
b. scene
c. heal
d. allowed
e. jeans
f. sweet

Solution to Puzzle Found
Across
2. plaza
3. burro
4. conversation
7. pronto
8. tortillas
Down
1. rodeo
2. patio
3. bronco
5. vanilla
6. tacos

Score Higher on Tests
1. B
2. C
3. B
4. D
5. A
6. D
7. B
8. B
9. B
10. D
11. B
12. C

Space Technology Improves Life on Earth
pages 13-17

Do You Read Me?
We get many new products from the space program.

Alphabet Shows Word Order
1. applications
2. consumer
3. encased
4. pollutants
5. potential
6. purifiers
7. recreation
8. savor
9. technology
10. video

Link Found Between Words and Meanings
1. i
2. b
3. d
4. f
5. a
6. g
7. e
8. h
9. j
10. c

Completed Sentences Make Meaning Clear
1. encased
2. savor
3. technology
4. applications
5. video

6. consumer
7. recreation
8. potential
9. purifiers
10. pollutants

Synonyms Are Closely Related
1. entire
2. humorous
3. expression
4. shatter
5. exceptional
6. muscular
7. nasty
8. permit

Riddle Brings New Technology to Light
1. applications
2. recreation
3. consumer
4. technology
5. encased
6. savor
7. pollutants
8. video
9. challenge
10. energy

Test-day Tips Told
1. B
2. D
3. B
4. D
5. B
6. A
7. C
8. A
9. C
10. D
11. A
12. D

Remedy for Hiccups Still a Mystery
pages 18-22

Main Idea Found in Story
what happens in your body when you hiccup

Alphabet Puts Words in Order
1. abruptly
2. cavity
3. contractions
4. diaphragm
5. familiar
6. hiccup
7. remedies
8. rhythmic
9. spasm
10. spinal cord

Words and Meanings—A Perfect Match
1. b
2. d
3. f
4. h
5. i
6. g
7. e
8. c
9. j
10. a

Words Fill Incomplete Sentences
1. hiccup
2. contractions
3. familiar
4. rhythmic
5. cavity
6. spinal cord
7. spasm
8. diaphragm
9. abruptly
10. remedies

Opposites Attract
1. minor
2. strange
3. minimum
4. gradually
5. smooth
6. expansions
7. positive
8. informed
9. artificial
10. sell

Search Is on for Hidden Words

Improve Your Score
1. C
2. C
3. B
4. A
5. A
6. D
7. A
8. C
9. B
10. B
11. D
12. C

Toni Morrison—Nobel Prize Winner
pages 23-27

One Thing Leads to Another
Toni won the Nobel Prize.

The Amazing Alphabet
1. childhood
2. distinguished
3. established
4. folklore
5. graduated
6. inspires
7. journalism
8. literature
9. Nobel Prize
10. publishing

Words and Meanings—A Prize-Winning Match
1. a   6. h
2. c   7. f
3. e   8. d
4. g   9. j
5. i   10. b

New Words Finish Sentences
1. childhood
2. journalism
3. publishing
4. graduated
5. established
6. distinguished
7. literature
8. folklore
9. inspires
10. Nobel Prize

Suffixes Give Words Happy Endings
1. investigative
2. aggressive
3. descriptive
4. supportive
5. persuasive
6. narrative
7. active
8. explosive
9. expensive

Big Brainstorm Headed This Way!
Answers will vary.

Secrets to Success on Tests
1. B
2. C
3. D
4. C
5. A
6. D
7. B
8. C
9. D
10. B
11. B
12. B

The Eyes Have It
pages 33-37

The Truth About Blinking
1. True   3. True
2. False   4. False

The Amazing Alphabet
1. blinking   6. mucus
2. fluid   7. secrete
3. germs   8. security
4. glands   9. skull
5. irritate   10. tear

Words and Meanings Go Together
1. c   6. i
2. b   7. e
3. f   8. j
4. g   9. d
5. h   10. a

Words Complete Sentences
1. blinking   6. germs
2. irritate   7. security
3. tear   8. mucus
4. secrete   9. skull
5. fluid   10. glands

Suffixes Change Word Meaning
1. workable   5. flexible
2. laughable   6. chewable
3. usable   7. teachable
4. lovable   8. combustible

Analogies Make Meaningful Relationships
1. skull
2. tear
3. fluid
4. germs
5. security

Test-taking Secrets Revealed
1. D
2. B
3. A
4. D
5. B
6. C
7. D
8. B
9. B
10. C
11. D
12. B

Mountain Bikers Conquer the Earth
pages 28-32

Readers Pick Best Title
What Is Mountain Biking?

Alphabet Keeps Words in Order
1. alterations   6. intimidate
2. built   7. maneuver
3. competitive   8. refurbished
4. coordination 9. suspensions
5. endurance   10. terrain

Words and Meanings—A Perfect Match
1. e   6. a
2. d   7. g
3. h   8. f
4. i   9. c
5. b   10. j

Incomplete Sentences Need Help from New Words
1. intimidate
2. coordination
3. maneuver
4. terrain
5. competitive
6. alterations
7. refurbished
8. built
9. suspensions
10. endurance

Drawing the Line with Synonyms
1. a   11. d
2. b   12. e
3. c   13. a
4. e   14. b
5. d   15. c
6. d   16. e
7. c   17. c
8. e   18. a
9. b   19. b
10. a   20. d

Scrambled Words Finally Sorted Out
1. coordination
2. competitive
3. endurance
4. alterations
5. built
6. maneuver
7. refurbished
8. terrain
9. suspensions
10. intimidate

Test Your Best
1. B   7. B
2. D   8. C
3. D   9. A
4. B   10. C
5. C   11. B
6. D   12. C

Misunderstood Mammal Needs Our Help
pages 38-42

Sequence Revealed
listens for an echo

Alphabet Keeps Words Under Control

amount	*inseam*
annoy	insecticides
annual	mammals
clicking	*pesky*
echoes	pests
enviable	populations
environment	species
image	*spectator*

Words Match Meanings
1. d   6. b
2. h   7. a
3. f   8. e
4. i   9. j
5. c   10. g

New Words Click with Incomplete Sentences
1. annoy
2. environment
3. clicking
4. image
5. Insecticides
6. mammals
7. echoes
8. populations
9. pests
10. species

Prefixes Create a Whole New Meaning
1. subspecies
2. supermarkets
3. superstructure
4. subsoil
5. subnormal

Puzzling Behavior
Across
1. species
4. populations
6. echoes
8. environment
10. annoy
Down
2. image
3. insecticides
5. clicking
7. pests
9. mammals

Score Higher on Tests
1. A
2. B
3. D
4. D
5. C
6. B
7. B
8. C
9. C
10. A
11. B
12. D

Get a Kick Out of the Martial Arts
pages 43-47

What's Your Opinion?
1. O
2. F
3. O
4. F

Alphabet Builds Word Order
adapt
aggressive
boisterous
combination
confidence
conscientious
count
industrious
intruder
join
martial arts
respect
seldom
self-defense
threatening

Words and Meanings—A Perfect Match
1. b
2. h
3. d
4. i
5. f
6. j
7. e
8. c
9. g
10. a

New Words Zero in on Sentence Holes
industrious
martial arts
respect
boisterous
intruder
threatening
aggressive
conscientious
self-defense
confidence

Suffixes Change Word Meanings
1. excitement
2. agreement
3. enjoyment
4. amazement
5. development
6. assignment

Riddle Reveals Mysterious Artist
1. boisterous
2. industrious
3. intruder
4. confidence
5. respect
6. self-defense
7. threatening
8. aggressive
Bruce Lee

Test-day Tips Told
1. C
2. D
3. B
4. A
5. C
6. B
7. C
8. D
9. C
10. B
11. D
12. A

Nothing Fishy About This Whale Tale
pages 48-52

Fact or Opinion? You Be the Judge
1. F
2. O
3. O
4. F

Alphabet Makes Order for Words
about
actually
acute
appetite
constantly
enormous
enough
oxygen
quantities
resembles
reserve
resident
satin
satisfy
ton

Words and Meanings Make Satisfying Match
1. d
2. f
3. a
4. g
5. c
6. i
7. h
8. b
9. j
10. e

New Words Fill Enormous Sentence Holes
1. actually, resembles
2. constantly, enormous
3. quantities, ton
4. resident, oxygen
5. satisfy, appetite

Reader Finds Synonyms Are Similar
1. d
2. c
3. a
4. e
5. b
6. b
7. a
8. d
9. e
10. c
11. c
12. a
13. d
14. b
15. e
16. c
17. d
18. a
19. e
20. b

Word Search Reveals New Words

```
U G E H O L D C O N S T
Q R E S E M B L E S N A
U C N L T Q U A N T O P
A R O T I O F O Q Y A P
N E R N D O N X O E R E
T T M E S M B Y A L S T
I S O X Y T E G N C A I
T A U N L Y A E F O T T
I Y S A T I S N I N I E
E R E S I D E N T O S T
S A C T U A L L Y L E N
L E Q U N T I T E O Y S
```

Improve Your Score
1. B
2. C
3. B
4. A
5. D
6. C
7. B
8. D
9. B
10. A
11. C
12. C

Native American Code Helps Win Battle
pages 53-57

Solve the Main Idea Mystery
Navajos developed an important secret code.

The Alphabet—A Code for Order
about
announces
attract
breaks
code
crimson
error
reservation
respect
responds
transformed
translations
transmitted
transportation
unbreakable

Words and Meanings Make a Match
1. a
2. i
3. e
4. j
5. f
6. h
7. c
8. d
9. b
10. g

New Words Transform Incomplete Sentences
1. responds
2. announces
3. code
4. breaks
5. reservation
6. translations
7. transformed
8. unbreakable
9. transmitted
10. error

Word Meanings Multiply
1. b
2. a
3. b
4. a
5. a
6. b
7. b
8. a

Brainstorm Bursting with Ideas
Answers will vary.

Secrets to Success on Tests
1. C
2. B
3. C
4. C
5. C
6. A
7. C
8. D
9. B
10. C
11. D
12. A

Mark Your Calendar for Hundreds of Holidays!
pages 58-62

Just the Facts, Please
1. O
2. F
3. O
4. F

Alphabet Promotes New Word Order
about
authority
calendar
consonant
frustrations
holiday
hunt
observation
promote
report
siblings
sponsors
surroundings
talent
unconventional

Words and Meanings—A Match to Celebrate
1. j
2. i
3. d
4. f
5. h
6. b
7. g
8. e
9. c
10. a

Missing Words Go Back to Work
holiday
calendar
unconventional
authority
sponsors
surroundings
Siblings
frustrations
observation
promote

Suffixes Cause New Meaning Sensation
a. create, act of creating
b. construct, act of constructing
c. inspect, act of inspecting
d. confuse, state of being confused
e. translate, a thing that is translated
f. complete, act of completing
g. express, a thing that is expressed
h. reflect, a thing that is reflected
i. act, state of acting

Unscramble the Mixed-up Words
1. frustrations
2. holiday
3. observation
4. calendar
5. siblings
6. unconventional
7. sponsors
8. authority
9. surroundings
10. promote

Test Your Best
1. B
2. C
3. A
4. B
5. B
6. B
7. C
8. A
9. C
10. C
11. D
12. B

Australians Rock On!
pages 63-67

What's the Point?
Yothu Yindi blends music and cultures, using Aboriginal music and Western rock-and-roll.

The Amazing Alphabet
adorn
ancient
coastal
contact
continent
culture
exhale

hermit
honored
inhale
preach
remark
remote
tolerance

Words and Meanings—A Perfect Match
1. h
2. c
3. d
4. a
5. g
6. f
7. b
8. j
9. i
10. e

Missing Words Found!
1. preach
2. inhale
3. remote
4. ancient
5. contact
6. honored
7. exhale
8. tolerance
9. coastal
10. culture

Homonyms—Rhyme but No Reason
1. patience
2. ore
3. bridal
4. sense
5. dew
6. gait

Meet the Analogy Challenge
1. honored
2. ancient
3. inhale
4. exhale
5. remote
6. preach

Test-taking Secrets Revealed
1. B
2. B
3. A
4. C
5. B
6. A
7. B
8. D
9. B
10. B
11. D
12. D

Skaters Get In-line for Fun
pages 73-77

Gliding into the Main Idea
In-line skating is a fun new trend in sports.

Save Room for More Words
abacus/fight
absorb
equipment
figment/intern
figures
glinting
intermediate
practice/transmission
propelled
rent
transport/whittle
transportation
trend
whirring

Words and Meanings Make Close Match
1. g
2. j
3. b
4. a
5. e
6. c
7. i
8. f
9. d
10. h

Filling in the Gaps
1. transportation
2. trend
3. intermediate
4. propelled
5. whirring
6. figures
7. rent
8. equipment
9. glinting
10. absorb

Antonyms—Opposites Attract
1. destroy
2. weak
3. peaceful
4. part
5. leave
6. stale
7. release
8. unusual
9. tough
10. innocent
11. expensive
12. shiny
13. wild
14. vanish
15. love
16. straight
17. melt
18. horizontal
19. success
20. false
21. exit
22. wise
23. rude
24. rich

Be a Super Sleuth
1. transportation
2. equipment
3. whirring
4. glinting
The Hidden Message:
Let's go skating in the park.

Test-day Tips Told
1. B
2. C
3. D
4. B
5. B
6. B
7. A
8. C
9. A
10. B
11. B
12. A

Biosphere II—Life in a Bubble
pages 68-72

Can You Describe It?
palace

The Amazing Alphabet
action/emblem
airtight
confined
ecosystem
glide/jar
habitats
inordinate
rain/trumpet
recycled
replica
self-contained
structure
terrarium

Words and Meanings Make a Match
1. e
2. h
3. f
4. i
5. a
6. d
7. g
8. b
9. c
10. j

Missing Word Alert!
1. replica
2. structure
3. terrarium
4. recycled
5. confined
6. self-contained
7. habitats
8. ecosystem
9. airtight
10. inordinate

Suffixes Make Big Word Changes
1. apologize
2. realize
3. colonize
4. generalize
5. formalize
6. Americanize
7. popularize
8. vaporize

Crossword Puzzler
Across
4. inordinate
5. habitats
7. replica
8. ecosystem
9. terrarium
Down
1. airtight
2. confined
3. structure
6. self-contained
7. recycled

Score Higher on Tests
1. A
2. D
3. C
4. C
5. A
6. C
7. B
8. B
9. D
10. B
11. C
12. C

Avalanche!
pages 78-82

Conclusions Formed
The avalanche would damage the town.

Guide Words Keep Dictionary on Track
billion/demerit
billows
concrete
democrat/forbear
demolishing
destination
dramatic
forbid/occasion
force
gravity
occupy/various
occurs
slab
variety

Words and Meanings
1. b
2. d
3. a
4. f
5. h
6. i
7. g
8. j
9. c
10. e

New Paragraph Finally Complete
destination
demolishing
variety
slab
force
concrete
Gravity
dramatic
billows
occurs

Break Words into Syl-la-bles
1. va ri e ty
2. dra mat ic
3. des ti na tion
4. de mol ish
5. bil low
6. con crete
7. grav i ty
8. av a lanche
9. ex cla ma tion
10. pop u la tion

Word Search
```
S I T U A L I S H I O N
F D F C O R O E V A R I
D E M O L I S H I N G E
R S O N R B I L L O W S
A T Y C S C L G A B S L
M I F R C R E R C B O E
A N C E N U C A R E C T
T A C T O N C V R E C S
I T D E S T N I A T U N
C I V A R I E T Y O R S
D O R A M A T Y I C S T
S N L A B B I L L O S W
```

Improve Your Score
1. A
2. B
3. D
4. B
5. A
6. B
7. C
8. A
9. C
10. B
11. D
12. B

111

"Terror Bird" Once Roamed North America
pages 83-87

What's in a Name?
had a frightening appearance.

Explore the Dictionary with Guide Words
bingo/incalculable
binoculars
confusion
incandescent/nice
incapable
item
mammoth
nickel/regard
nicknamed
obtained
regimen/stuck
regions
required
stubby

Avoid Confusion—Match Words with Meanings Now

1.	f	6.	d
2.	c	7.	g
3.	i	8.	b
4.	j	9.	e
5.	a	10.	h

Missing Words Come Home to Roost
mammoth
stubby
binoculars
item
incapable
regions
nicknamed
confusion
obtained
required

Prefixes—A New Beginning
uni unicycle
uni uniform
bi bimonthly
bi bicycle
bi biannual
tri triangle
tri tricycle

Big Brainstorm Headed This Way
Answers will vary.

Secrets to Success on Tests

1.	D	7.	B
2.	B	8.	A
3.	D	9.	D
4.	C	10.	B
5.	D	11.	C
6.	A	12.	C

Poison Plant Plot Exposed
pages 88-92

Readers Itching About Inferences
already shelled

Guide Words Help Keep Order
beverage/itself
beware
disguises
ivory/plight
ivy
ounce
plop/sound
plot
produce
rash
soup/unfounded
source
typical
unfortunately

Words and Meanings Produce Perfect Match

1.	e	6.	f
2.	a	7.	d
3.	i	8.	h
4.	c	9.	g
5.	j	10.	b

Missing Words Make Sentences Complete
1. source
2. disguises
3. typical
4. Unfortunately
5. beware
6. ounce
7. produce
8. rash
9. ivy
10. plot

Prefixes Add New Meaning
a. unfortunate, not fortunate
b. unacceptable, not acceptable
c. unafraid, not afraid
d. unbeaten, not beaten
e. nonprofit, not making profit
f. nonsense, not making sense
g. nonresident, not a resident
h. nonstop, not making a stop

Analogies Show Word Relationships
1. rash
2. produce
3. beware
4. ounce
5. typical
6. ivy

Secrets to Success on Tests

1.	B	7.	D
2.	B	8.	B
3.	B	9.	C
4.	C	10.	C
5.	A	11.	B
6.	C	12.	A

Woman Trades Tennis Racket for Space Racket
pages 93-97

Story Says More Than Meets the Eye!
Sally's decision to become an astronaut led to a successful career.

Guide Words Tell the Score
abacus/foam
abandoned
ambition
career
focal/observe
focused
historical
mechanical
obtain/rock
occasion
retrieve
rodeo/taste
satellite
task

Words and Meanings Match

1.	d	6.	b
2.	a	7.	e
3.	g	8.	c
4.	j	9.	i
5.	h	10.	f

Sentences Take Off with Word Power!
1. historical
2. abandoned
3. career
4. ambition
5. occasion
6. satellite
7. task
8. focused
9. mechanical
10. retrieve

Homonyms Serve Up Trouble for Careless Readers
1. role
2. aisle
3. flair
4. pedal
5. knight

Readers Unscramble Word Mix-up
1. occasion
2. retrieve
3. abandoned
4. focused
5. mechanical
6. task
7. ambition
8. career
9. historical
10. satellite

Test-taking Secrets Revealed

1.	D	7.	B
2.	C	8.	D
3.	D	9.	D
4.	B	10.	C
5.	A	11.	C
6.	D	12.	A

Rugged Bikes Put Kids in the Race
pages 98-102

Nothing Wild About This Guess
BMX riders need heavy-duty clothing to prevent injury.

Guide Words Keep Dictionary Organized
adamant/feast
adapted
dealer
designed
feather/knife
feature
initials
knit/rude
knobby
operate
organized
ruffle/style
rugged
sturdy

Words and Meanings Were Meant to Match

1.	e	6.	d
2.	h	7.	g
3.	c	8.	b
4.	j	9.	f
5.	a	10.	i

Missing Words Designed to Fill Sentence Blanks
1. dealer, initials
2. organized, rugged
3. designed, adapted
4. sturdy, knobby
5. feature, operate

Alphabet Soup

1.	f	5.	a
2.	b	6.	e
3.	c	7.	d
4.	h	8.	g

The Great Puzzle Race Is On
Across
1. designed
6. organized
8. adapted
9. sturdy
10. feature
Down
2. dealer
3. knobby
4. rugged
5. initials
7. operate

Score Higher on Tests

1.	B	7.	B
2.	D	8.	D
3.	C	9.	B
4.	A	10.	B
5.	C	11.	D
6.	A	12.	C